G000043277

TEARS
AFTER
DARK

Sally Whiteside

Pen Press Publishers
London

TEARS AFTER DARK

Sally Whiteside

First published in Great Britain by
Pen Press Publishers Ltd
39-41 North Road
Islington
London N7 9DP

ISBN 1 900796 71 6

Printed in Great Britain by
Antony Rowe Ltd, Chippenham, Wilts

Cover design by Catrina Sherlock
from an original drawing by Marc Whiteside

'It matters not how strait the gate
How charged with punishment the scroll
I am the master of my fate:
I am the captain of my soul.'

W E Henley 1849 - 1903

for Tom
with love always

About the Author

Sally Whiteside was brought up in Surrey, the eldest of three children, and was educated in Purley. She has written many competition-winning short stories over the past twenty years, but this is her first completed novel. Having worked for Surrey Young Carers Project, Sally realises just how many young carers there are and hopes that some will empathise with *Tears After Dark*, a predominantly true story.

Besides writing, the author is a keen amateur photographer. She also draws and enjoys music, is a keen piano player and is currently learning the clarinet.

Sally Whiteside lives in Horley with husband Tom, several children and several dogs!

PREFACE

Why do I not hate her? After all she did to us, or allowed to happen to us, I still can not find hate in my heart.

Perhaps I have gone through some type of therapy all by myself, come to terms with everything that happened to us as children, laid to rest all those ghosts of the past.

There comes a time, on reaching adulthood, when everyone makes a decision, in true existential form: which way is my life going to go? We were bred to be the delinquents and criminals of tomorrow - we have all the text book excuses.

Sometimes, when I smell the right smell or catch a glimpse of someone a little familiar, I find myself reflecting on days long gone. It is still so easy to think back, to cast aside the years and remember my very earliest memories - like the first time I saw a new born baby when my little brother was born in 1959. I was aged three years and ten months when he made his arrival and it is practically my first memory.

There are some stories that just have to be told....

Chapter 1

A little summer's sun light shone through the thin curtains at my bedroom window. It streamed across the room and hit a picture of Jesus with a crown of thorns on his head, lighting it up in brilliant white glory. But he had a sad disillusioned face, as if he carried all the burdens of the world on his shoulders, which I suppose, as a good Catholic boy, I had to believe he did.

*'Thank you God Our Father for the home where I live,
Thank you for my mummy and daddy who love me and
look after me.'*

It had been a strange night - a lot of footsteps and noise outside my door and I had not slept well. My brother did not seem to have been bothered by the whispering and shuffling about. Twice I had called softly out to him but he had not stirred. I was just wondering about getting up when the door slowly opened.

My dad peeped his head round, a bit flushed, grinning at me. 'Come in here, Terry,' he said gently. 'Come and see what mum's got!'

I pushed the blanket back and padded across the linoed floor and he put his big hand on the back of my head, guiding me towards her, then stood behind me as we went into the other bedroom. Propped up in bed by two enormous stripy pillows was mum, smiling, cradling a tiny bundle. She removed one hand to pat the bed next to her and I took that as my invitation to jump up beside her. She put her arm round me and cuddled me too.

'Look,' she said. 'Your new baby brother. Thank our Father for his safe arrival.' Rosary beads were entwined in her fingers underneath the new baby's feet.

We stayed like that for quite a while and she stroked my head as we sat there. I looked at the new baby carefully. He had a small red wrinkled face which he screwed up every now and again. It seemed impossible to imagine that he could ever be a boy like me - not that I even thought that far ahead. I could feel the warmth of my mum's body against my side and I noticed her fair hair was slightly damp and dishevelled, which was not like her. She was always well-kept and her hair was usually combed exactly into place. Dad hovered around bringing cups of tea and pieces of toast which mum never touched. He tried really hard to be part of this very special time.

My dad was a big man - a miner, son of a quarryman, brother of miners and quarrymen and he simply towered above my mum who was barely five feet tall. That was the employment here - working on the new roads and the intended site of Glasgow airport and mining for coal. Dad worked down the pit, often on nights because that was more pay. He was young and strong and ready for hard work and he believed passionately in providing for his family. He wanted us to grow up good Catholic boys and we all went to chapel every Sunday. Father was father to us all.

Dad wore enormous boots and would offer Jack and me a foot each every morning when he got home and we would pull and pull to get them off. Once I had stepped into them but I could hardly lift a foot, let alone walk.

I am sure that we were a contented family in those early days. We were living in impecunious circumstances but we were part of a close community in the tiny village of Bridgend, just outside Glasgow, where everyone knew everyone else. All the children played together out in the street and the wives all gossiped and chatted from their doorsteps. We lived right in the middle of a long row of red brick miner's cottages, just two rooms and a kitchen really and we had a black front door with a brightly polished red brick step.

In the distance, up on the hill, we could just make out the wheels of the mine, often slowly turning as the shifts changed. I think we knew then that we were all destined to go down that pit - it was our future too. Our lives went on uninterrupted in the shadow of the mine. We were so safe - nothing could touch us.

****

My dad was the youngest of eight and my mum one of nine. Her family were the dominant characters in our young lives as they lived locally in nearby Chryston. Two of her brothers were miners - only one had moved away from the area. Her mother was a solid woman - strong, Scottish stock who ruled her offspring with a rod of iron, before and after marriage. Her hair was always drawn back into a loose bun at the nape of her neck and she would squint and stare at us through tiny round spectacles. She was rarely disobeyed and she felt she had done right by all her children. She had been a widow for fifteen years and all her children were employed, married and housed and that was a success story. My mum, Alice, was her sixth child and probably the one who was closest to her in those early days.

Alice had married for love - everybody said so. She had met my dad, Terry senior, several years before at the local dances, when she was in her early twenties. He was the same age as her, tall, fair and handsome. He was musical, could play a tune on any instrument, could sing and dance and was just that little bit better educated than her. He could even get a tune out of the big saw up at the pit! He knew how to give a girl a good night out and Alice lapped up all the attention that she had never received, being part of such a large family.

She had her eye on him as a prospective husband very early on. They sang and danced together and everyone said they made a lovely couple.

Apart from a few months in 1949 when Alice had worked in a hotel in Largs, they had never really been apart and no one was surprised when they could eventually afford to get married in July 1953. Within a year Jack had been born, followed sixteen months later by Terry junior and now, four years on, they had baby Angus.

I think in her younger days she had been an attractive, though painfully shy woman - never short of a boyfriend or two, but she quickly realised that she was much better company after a couple of drinks. Then, she thought she was fun and high spirited and worthy of the men who took her out. As the years went by we heard the story of how she almost ran off with a hotel owner from Largs - a married man who was going to abandon all for her. But something happened and she decided her initial instincts were right: she missed Terry and moved back to Chryston. He was her man, she decided, almost totally single-mindedly and after they married she settled happily into the role of wife and mother.

I do not think my mum ever wanted any more children. After Angus was born she could often be heard saying that there would be no more. She had her boys and that was enough. She took pleasure in hanging out rows of dazzling white nappies in the back yard and occasionally going for walks with Angus in a big black pram. Jack and I used to trail behind and sit and play in the dirt when she stopped for a chat with someone.

Jack started school at the beginning of September and we slipped into a routine revolving round walks to school and back again. Sometimes when we arrived back after school we could hear the gentle tunes of a harmonica or a fiddle wafting up the road and it would be dad, playing a tune, while waiting for the kettle to boil. We would all sit round the kitchen table and sing along. They were such carefree, happy days. I wanted to wrap myself up in all the security and I never wanted it all to end.

****

On the morning of Friday, September 18th, 1959, dad had left home at 6.30am for a day shift. We had heard many men marching past our cottage on their way to the pit, heard their voices, their laughing and occasional whistling. Jack and I were up now, drinking milk and eating toast.

Rap...rap...rap urgently on the front door. Mum walked over and opened it. We heard a man's voice and she stepped outside, pulling the door closed behind her. I heard her voice - slightly shrill, then I could hear other people, further away down the road, shouting and men were running past the front of our house. I climbed up onto the sofa and looked out. Yes, everyone was running up towards the pit. On the horizon I could see a trail of thick black smoke. That was strange - I had never seen smoke up there before.

Then Auntie Jean from next door burst in and our mum was gone. We could see her now, hurrying up towards the pit as well, still putting her arm into the sleeve of her coat. Jack and I turned and looked at Auntie Jean. She was crying. She gathered us up into her ample bosom and cried some more.

'Oh you poor wee boys,' she kept saying. 'Please God that everything will be all right for you. You poor wee boys.'

Jack and I looked at each other over the top of her grubby apron and grinned. She squeezed us so tightly. She had loads of children of her own and I wondered if she squeezed all of them so much.

Up at the pithead of Auchengeich Colliery the dusty paths began filling up with the womenfolk, to start what became a long wait. The news was sketchy but it seemed that there had been a fire one thousand feet underground, and it appeared to have trapped a wagon of forty eight men. No one knew for sure if there were any survivors but men in boiler suits and helmets were desperately trying to put out the fire. They themselves reappeared scorched and had to be hosed down as their three inch boots melted on their feet. Our priest had appeared and was talking quietly to small groups of waiting women, some of whom clutched rosary beads and whispered prayers to themselves.

Much later we found out exactly what had happened. At seven o'clock the day shift had arrived for work. Fifty men had clambered into the first cage and travelled the thousand feet to the pit bottom. They had then climbed into a waiting bogie, a wagon that would take them down to the coal face where they were working. A winding engine man had started hauling them along the mile they had to go.

A second cage had reached the pit bottom and our dad had been one of the forty eight men who had climbed into their waiting bogie. One man had said he could smell smoke but they had been sufficiently confident to continue to the coal face. The driver had been signalled with a bell and gradually they moved down the first gradient.

About four hundred yards along they hit a blanket of carbon monoxide smoke. A fan belt further along, controlling the ventilation shaft had slipped off its pulley and the friction had set it on fire. The first bogie of men were able to ride through the impenetrable gas known as 'white damp' and had escaped through an air tight door into an air shaft. But the second group had not been so fortunate. There was no way of stopping their bogie which continued for a further half a mile. Their lamps would have shown the gas as a solid white wall.

Some men shouted out, they coughed and spluttered frantically. The winding engine man could himself smell smoke and he began winding them backwards to safety. But then he had been overcome by the fumes and had collapsed, leaving the doomed men entombed just three hundred yards away. The fire raged for fourteen hours. One hundred and fifty rescue workers battled to reach the trapped men while fires so hot that steel pit props melted, burnt one thousand feet below.

That morning my mum waited with the other women and relatives of those forty eight trapped men. Some of the wives were in slippers, wearing curlers in their hair, still with their aprons on. They stood desolate in the morning sunshine, their faces blank with the terrible fears of disaster. Two pithead wheels turned ceaselessly in the vain attempts at rescue while smoke continued to seep out from the fire below.

All day the women came and waited. There was no screaming or hysterics that morning. Occasionally someone would sob quietly but they were a self-controlled group, an astonishingly disciplined crowd of mining women, feeling their widowhood before it was confirmed, their worst nightmares had become reality.

A young blackened man collapsed into his grandmother's arms. He had been feared dead but he had been in the first bogie and was safe. It had been a seven hours wait to see him but one family was rejoicing. An ambulance suddenly erupted into action and sped off down the dusty path, bell clanging! The news spread quickly - one man had escaped the holocaust. Who was he? Whose husband or son was safe? Several hours later his name seeped round and my mum knew it was not her man.

The Salvation Army helpers, that great traditional source of comfort and hope, had been dishing out tea by the canteen to tear-stained relatives, forcing people to eat and drink while trying to say the right comforting words.

At some point during the day my gran had come and collected Jack and me from the kindly Auntie Jean and we had joined our mum at the pithead at Auchengeich. Gran had two sons in the rescue team and she stood stolidly by my mum, waiting for news.

'Dear God, Our Father, you love all the things that you have made,
You love my daddy - please keep him safe.'

All the scattered villages surrounding the colliery were paying the toll of lives that day - Gartferry, Chryston, Muirhead,

Bridgend. So many families began grieving - an intense private grief, whilst hugging their children to their hips and waiting.

Day began to turn into night. Gran took us back to her house where we were tucked up into makeshift beds on the floor. At 9pm, as the damp blanket of darkness slowly wrapped itself around us all, the Coal Board officially announced that they considered the chances of finding any survivors negligible and arrangements were in hand to flood part of the mine. There seemed no other way of putting out the fire.

Mum was led away by her two brothers and a sister-in-law. She was numb with shock, almost unable to walk and they held her up and comforted her as best they could. She felt her life was over, that she too should die with Terry. Indeed if it had not been for her three boys I think she would have ended it all that night. But she knew she had to carry on.

Dad was just thirty two when he died, Angus only six weeks. There had been no goodbyes.

A couple of weeks later a parade of coffins on the backs of carts towed by black horses, went down Bridgend Road. Forty seven coffins take a long time to go past and Jack and I sat at the window and watched them. Our big clock stopped ticking for ever as one particular coffin went by and mum said dad was in that one.

The little chapel held the funeral services - up to ten coffins at a time were in there. It was a devastatingly sad time for everyone - so many families affected, so many children fatherless. Even thirty years later it was remembered poignantly when a new memorial was built near to the mine. There was never an incident to match it for the cruelty and absolute waste of life.

The disaster changed the course of all our lives. The pit never re-opened, the Coal Board were blasted for their negligence and bad maintenance was blamed for the fire. Effectively the whole community was broken up as we all had to move. We were to move to a newer, bigger house a mile or so away. Our gran had taken control of baby Angus and at times we forgot he existed. Mum seemed to be coping. We were dressed and fed and Jack went to school, but we were surrounded by a sadness that just would not go away and an anger that was often directed at us.

Uncle Jim had become a frequent visitor, often staying for days. He was mum's younger brother, a tough hard Glasweigan whose life revolved round the working men's club in Bridgend. Many a night we heard him talking to mum, trying to convince her that Angus should stay with his gran for good. We lay in bed hearing her answering him angrily, that she would never give up one of her boys - they were all she had left of Terry. Usually the conversations ended the same way. Uncle Jim would say: 'Well, say what you will, but I can't see how a woman can cope with three young boys without a man to provide for her. Come on now hen, let's go up the club......' We would hear the click of the front door and they would be gone. Our mornings often became 'look after yourself' mornings as Uncle Jim and mum slept in, recovering from their late night. Mum was finding that alcohol blotted out her intense sadness, drowned that feeling of hopelessness and loneliness and gave her an outside skin of strength and cheerfulness that she had hidden behind years before.

We were moved to our new house in December and it was agreed that Angus should live with his gran indefinitely. Mum was not a well-educated woman and I think the fear of poverty and homelessness forced her decision. There was no social security as there is today and she was desperate to keep her family together. Jack and I had a new bedroom, all to ourselves - not one room divided into two like our cottage in Bridgend, but a real four-roomed house. I still remember the day we moved, and the old van that took our few belongings up the hill in a cloud of black smoke. As we left our little miner's cottage I remember seeing mum's rosary beads lying in the dirt outside and for a second I hesitated, wondering whether I should retrieve them, but then someone yelled at me to move aside and a cart laden with furniture was dragged by and the beads

were crushed further into the mud. Mum's hand quickly
grabbed mine and pulled me away. She never looked back.
There were still familiar faces around us as we settled into our
new house, for many Bridgend families had also moved to
these pre-fabs. Even though we were now closer to our gran,
we did not see Angus again for years.

Chapter 2

Christmas 1959 was one massive party for all our relatives and anyone who even remotely knew us. A disaster fund had been set up and money from well-wishers all over the world had flooded in. Newspaper reporters had milled about with notepads and pens, trying to buy stories off anyone who would talk to them. Hawkers tried to sell gravestones to widows. It was a strange mercenary time.

Now the payouts had been made and the fund had been closed. Each widow received £2000 and each fatherless child was to receive £13 per month until their eighteenth birthday. Everyone, including our mum, pledged that the money, a small fortune in those days, would, of course, be put into trust for the children. But first they had to party!

Jack and I watched as crates of drink were loaded on to the kitchen table. Strangers milled about. Men we had never seen before, painted ladies with bleached hair and red lips strutted around our little house and helped themselves to food and drink. Jack and I were bewildered by it all and much of Christmas we spent in our bedroom while the adults danced and drank. We assumed mum was somewhere around.

At Easter Jack asked why he was not going to school anymore and mum announced that she had not liked the school he was at and she had his name down for another. Jack cried and said he had left a jumper on his peg but mum laughed, almost hysterically, as she stubbed out a cigarette with a bony finger and said what did that matter? He could have twenty jumpers now if he wanted them - money was no object anymore. She needed advice badly on what to do with her money but she never asked for it - she never thought it could run out.

Mum's new circle of pals were purely fair weather friends, though she never saw this herself. They all frequented the local pubs and working men's clubs and, though officially still grieving, mum began to thoroughly enjoy her frequent nights at bingo. She was not a huge gambler but the thrill from her small wins was enough to entice her back time after time, and of course, there was the bar! Mum had always been a drinker, even when dad had been alive. They had always had their Friday night binges. While Jack and I were being bathed, dad would appear back with a brown paper bag full of bottles and that was the source of their pleasure once we were safely tucked up in bed. Sometimes I would creep out of bed and peep through the big heavy curtain that had divided our rooms in the little cottage. Mum was always the one who was really intoxicated, the one who just could not stop. She was always very talkative when drunk and her eyes were moist and reddened. Dad often seemed to be asleep in his chair while she droned on and on.

Now, occasionally she brought us back small toys she had won or chocolate bars. As the men drank and played darts so the women drank and played bingo - it started all so innocently, but usually Jack and I were left quite alone at home. Auntie Jean, who lived a few doors away, kept an eye on us from time to time and as the weeks turned into months she became more and more worried about the amount mum was drinking. We were far too young to realise what an alcoholic was but I can remember asking her once not to drink so much.

When mum could not find her way home one winter's evening in December 1960 and Auntie Jean found her banging on the wrong door, shouting obscenities, insisting it was her home (much to the great annoyance of the occupants who were shouting back at her from the window!), it became obvious to everyone concerned that a drink problem was on the horizon. Mum would not listen to a word anyone said and she argued violently with the only people who really cared and tried to reason with her. Even our gran saw her drunk several times and threatened her: 'Alice, hen, if you're not sober enough to care for your wee boys then I shall pass them to someone who is!'

Mum began to realise that her drinking had to be concealed and so she started hiding bottles round the house. She grabbed Jack and me roughly by the arms and swore us to secrecy, threatening us with living in the children's home, 'that wicked dirty place where you will be locked in dark cupboards and whipped', she said. When gran asked us if she was ever drunk at home, Jack and I looked at her with wide open eyes and insisted that she never drank, except when she went out. We lied for our mum and shielded her from the wrath of gran. We started our secret life there and then because we loved her and because we were frightened of the consequences should we be taken away. Mum drilled an intense fear of children's homes into us and whatever we saw, or lived through, we always knew that worse would happen if we were taken away. But I became very intuitive. I could tell if she had been drinking as soon as I walked into the house. Just the way she looked at us was enough, and of course, once she spoke, there was the alcohol on her breath.

Mum was always the type of woman who needed male company and even though dad had only been dead a matter of months, it did not take her long to find new boyfriends. Often the house would be full of predatory men, all eager to refill her empty glass. The first real boyfriend was a gardener at Glasgow hospital, and he tried his very best to make a little front garden of flowers for us. But boyfriends only lasted as long as they could take mum's heavy drinking, for once her initial charms wore off, her aggressive and antagonistic personality began to show. She was just too much for most of them.

Eventually, to keep the peace and to stop everyone nagging her, mum started going along to the local branch of Alcoholics Anonymous. Auntie Jean's brother-in-law was a counsellor there. He had been sober for three years and now he was helping others. Eddie was a really nice man who had put his life back together after reaching rock bottom. There were seven members at mum's regular Monday evening groups but she hated talking about herself and her problem (which she really thought was a figment of everyone's imagination anyway) and she fought any acknowledgement that the group was even remotely beneficial. She also had a long walk to get there and a long walk back again at night. Eventually, to stop her from giving up on the group, Eddie started giving her a lift home. We met him once or twice - he wore a suit and sat and chatted to mum about his family over a cup of tea before he left for home. He was a nice decent man and he seemed to care about mum and her family. She was in better condition than she had been for ages and both Jack and I began to feel quite warm and cared for.

Mum regularly went to her meetings for a couple of months, although she never really stopped drinking entirely. We were absolutely horrified when she and Eddie came reeling home one Monday night, both drunk, laughing and giggling about something! Apparently every time she got into his car she pleaded with him to join her for a drink and eventually he relented. He really wanted to prove that they could have a good night out without alcohol but somehow he fell under mum's spell and started drinking again. She literally drove him, mentally and physically, to drink and all those sober years were wiped out. He spent the night lying face down in the front garden and somehow drove himself home in the early hours.

The next week there was a new counsellor at the Monday meetings and also a new member - a man called Harry, who like her, thought his problem had been widely exaggerated by family and friends. One afternoon mum brought him home to meet us.

Harry was a wide boy in his early forties, a petty criminal who would steal milk from doorsteps and never leave a shop without something hidden inside his coat. He was recently widowed himself. Originally he came from Stirling but he now lived in Chapelhall and since the death of his wife had been a frequent customer of many local pubs. He was looking for good business. He wanted to make money more than anything else. It was pure avarice that initially attracted him to mum. His sister lived in Glasgow and was caring for his two sons. He must have spotted mum a mile off and he homed in on her like a bee to a honeypot. Between them they both decided the AA was a total waste of time, there was absolutely nothing wrong with enjoying a good drink and they never went again. Anyway, Harry had far more important things on his mind than worrying about the AA - mum was a wealthy woman and she needed his financial advice!

Mum sat in the kitchen one evening, high spirited and effusive - drink just giving a tinge of sparkle to her personality while Harry looked through various documents. She leant forward and tapped his paperwork with her knobbly finger.

'And do you know why I'm not going back to Alchie Club?' she giggled. Harry glanced up at her and grunted. 'Well I'll tell you why, Harry - I'll tell you why! It's because the place is full of drunks - and I'm not a drunk. I just like a wee drink sometimes and there's nothing wrong with that, is there?' Another grunt. 'And it's so silly - you know, Harry, don't you? You know how very, very silly it all is.....' she turned to Jack and me, with the theatrical exaggerated movements of a drunk, wanting us to agree with her. 'I am an alcoholic! That's what we all have to say. I said it! Aye, I said that' (and then, animatedly, she repeated it) - 'I am an alcoholic! But it's not true! Och, I just like a wee drink. I choose to have a wee drink, I don't have to. And that's the difference between all the drunks and me! I choose when I want a drink and they don't. They *have* to have a drink. So I'm not an alcoholic and they are. And I don't see why I should go there and lie, isn't that right boys? I've brought you up right, now, haven't I? You know not to tell lies and it wouldn't be right if I did.' Jack and I stared at her, totally confused, nodded and glanced from her to Harry. We hadn't a clue what she was talking about, but she wanted to see us agree with her. She poured out more neat gin into a chipped old mug and threw it down her throat in one go.

'So that's that sorted then. Harry, Harry, what are you doing? What are you looking at? Can't it wait til morning?' She rolled her head heavily over his chest, trying her best to be seductive and interesting.

He looked at her blandly, pushing her upright, and they lit cigarettes together, sharing a match and then he smiled. 'Honey, there's money to be dealt with first,' he said, then turned to us with his yellow, nicotine stained eyes. 'Boys - bed!' And that was most definitely the end of our evening - we were in bed within two minutes. Harry's hand round our heads and his stinking alcoholic breath spitting all over our faces was the last thing we wanted.

Harry was full of ideas as to how our mum should spend our money. He called it 'investing' and he would sift through piles of paperwork at the kitchen table as they shared their bottle of gin during the evenings. He strongly advised her to do so many things. It was all beyond her and she was totally out of her depth. She agreed to anything he suggested for she really was not that interested - she was happy to trust him.

Eventually Harry became the proud owner of a garage in nearby Coatbridge and one afternoon he arrived at our house with an ice cream van. Jack and I ran down the path. He opened the door and lifted us up inside.

'Well boys, what do you think?' he said. 'Want an ice each?'

'Pokey hats!' we both shouted and he produced two enormous cornets from his freezer. This was great! Ice creams all summer from our very own ice cream van. What could be better than this?

Another night a Zepha Zodiac car pulled up behind our ice cream van and Harry emerged from that too, grinning from ear to ear, his cheeks red with excitement. Again he took great delight in putting Jack and me on the back seat, he grabbed our mum and took us for a ride. He was an atrocious reckless driver whose eyes seemed to be everywhere but on the road ahead, but Jack and I were thrilled by it all. We did not know anyone who had a car - this was real classy living. We could, after all, see Harry as being the deliverer of good times.

Harry's home in Chapelhall was near Airdrie and he wanted us to move in with him. Mum was reluctant at first but as Harry got his feet more firmly into our lives she relented and one day we piled all our belongings into the car and a van and moved far away to another new home. This house was an improvement on the pre-fab and Jack and I were too young to be anything but excited by the changes all around us.

Harry was, to us, a big man with a shock of jet black hair. He was wide too, a thick set man who seemed to throw each leg forward as he walked. He was when sober, reasonably kind to we boys but he also had a violent temper hinged on a short fuse, which displayed itself all too easily after a few drinks - and Harry liked his drink, often and neat. At a very early age we learnt to judge his moods, weigh that up against how much he had had to drink and act accordingly. We in turn, were probably quite a nuisance to him in those early days but it was often he who drove Jack to school and once I even saw him chatting to my teacher at the school gates. I had never seen mum talk to a teacher once and I began to think that despite everything, Harry really cared about us.

Harry never seemed to miss his own two sons and he never really said much about them but occasionally he would leave us for a few days in Glasgow and we assumed he had gone to visit Michael and Richard.

The worst thing about Harry was that he fancied himself as a bit of a chef and would spend ages producing the most enormous quantities of vegetable soup in to which he would throw tons of barley. We were never allowed to leave any food and I, in particular, hated barely. Once he made me sit at the table for four hours because I had not finished my soup and although I was physically reaching on every mouthful, he never gave in. It was stone cold and greasy but it all had to go. As the weeks passed I managed to fool him by grabbing handfuls of the stuff and filling my pockets. He would think nothing of giving me a tremendous whipping with his belt if he ever found out so I had to be very careful where it was all disposed of!

The first time we witnessed Harry and mum having a fight Jack and I were terrified. It started with a discussion, then voices became raised, especially mum's, then they were shouting at each other wildly. Harry's face was red and fierce and he literally spat his words out, his heavy Scottish accent thicker than ever. Mum's voice became higher and shrill. She had two fine lines of pink on the top of each cheekbone and she managed to wriggle forward on her chair as she argued until she was perched on the edge, leaning forwards towards Harry, wagging her finger at him furiously. It was only a couple of steps to be able to touch him and she suddenly jumped up and slapped him hard. In a flash Harry retaliated, he just was not the type of man to take a beating from a woman and his slaps could easily knock mum backwards.

Jack and I sat huddled together on the sofa watching, hardly daring to breathe in case we moved and they saw us. But they had forgotten we existed, so intense was their arguing. I felt something on my cheek and found myself wiping away a lone tear as they tussled roughly with each other, colliding with furniture until the sheer bulk of Harry resulted in mum being knocked over. He bent down and slapped her hard round the head several times. Mum ended up on the floor behind her chair and Harry stormed out in a vile temper. Jack and I sat quite still, petrified, frozen in time. When eventually she managed to get herself up and sorted out, she escorted us brusquely up to bed. She did not mention the fight at all, it was as if she had forgotten all about it and we were really confused.

There were many nights after that when they argued after we had gone to bed. As they settled into each others company the very worst of their personalities came to the surface. So many nights Jack and I wept silent tears as we heard the terrible noises below. I would pull my blankets right over my head, screw my eyes up tightly and try to shut it all out. It was all so very frightening. Perhaps it was something to do with Jack and me. If only we could be really good boys perhaps they would like each other more - quite often the rows seemed to start over something Jack or I had said or done. Jack once whispered in the darkness of our room that he was quite worried that Harry would kill mum and then what would happen to us? That was the most awful thought - life without mum was beyond contemplation - for she was our security, what little of it we had. She meant more than anything else. Harry was therefore the instigator of violence and fear and mum was the victim.

Now that they had wheels, their drinking did not have to be restricted to 'carry outs' anymore - now they could visit the bars and pubs. Uncle Jim still featured in mum's life. He would take her out for a drink at lunchtime when Harry was out 'investing.' At weekends Harry and mum would set off on a pub crawl, Jack and me on the back seat, which was where we stayed for hours, parked in a car park outside a seedy pub. Occasionally Harry would stagger out with a bottle of pop for us and a bag of crisps each. Jack and I would take it in turns to climb over the seat into the front. I would hold the steering wheel and tug it from side to side - I was Stirling Moss!

Invariably, when the pub closed, they would appear at the door of the pub - usually mum first, her eyes fixed in front of her, making a bolt for the car. Harry would follow, absolutely livid about something, yelling abuse at her. Then the fighting would start. As he caught up with her she would turn and lash out at him. He would punch her back and before long they were screaming at each other in a full blown fight. People would watch from a distance, pull their collars up and walk on by. No one interfered and I cannot ever remember the police being called.

Eventually they would get into the car and Harry would drive home. He must have been very drunk and it never ceased to amaze Jack and me that he did not kill us all, as mum would hurl abuse and punches at him all the way home and he would retaliate just as violently. One night she spent the entire journey with her door open and one leg hanging out of the car, cursing and screaming that she was 'getting out of the fucking car and he had better stop!' But he did not stop, in fact he went faster, and we managed to hang on to her just enough to stop her being tossed out. Often we guessed that they must really hate each other, they argued and fought so much. We suspected so often that we would never see Harry again.

The day after a particularly vicious fight I started school and set off with Jack in my new uniform. Mum accompanied us with a black eye, split lip and dislocated fingers. I heard her telling people that she had fallen down the stairs and wondered why she was lying. A few nights later Harry told us we were not to call him Harry anymore - he was dad now.

My mum's family hated Harry more than the devil himself. They had refused to visit us long ago and told mum that she was never to bring him to their houses. The root of the problem was probably that he was a Protestant, but getting control of her money added to his marriage motives and their resentment. Also, some months before, Uncle Jim had walked in once while Harry was in the middle of punching the daylight out of mum. He had grabbed Harry and beaten him black and blue. I remember Harry being thrown over a chair and losing handfuls of hair and a tooth before he vanished for two days! All these things did not exactly endear him to mum's family.

Aware of the dislike he encountered with his new wife's relations, Harry needed to get Jack and me on his side. He needed us to need him and he wanted to impress. My sixth birthday was a few weeks away and he began to promise me the most wonderful birthday present. At school I needed to be liked and I began to tell everybody about the present I had been promised. Before long all the children were buzzing with the news that Terry Steer was getting his own helicopter!

Harry said he was having it specially made for me. I would be able to fly to school every day and my two new friends, Robert and Billy would be able to squeeze in (for it was only a two seater). We were going to go everywhere in my helicopter. My new dad was arranging it all. It was to have the best engine a helicopter could have, blue and white seats and a bright yellow propeller. I would be the only boy ever - in the whole world - to have such an advanced form of flight. I knew we had lots of money now, I knew dad had brought home lots of new things. I could not wait to see this helicopter.

Billy and Robert were as excited as me on the morning of my birthday. Dad took me to school, chuckling that my helicopter would be at home after school. As he left me with Billy he said he hoped I would be able to control my helicopter - it would have so much power. What a day! The best birthday present ever was going to be at my house after school. For the first and only time I invited Billy and Robert to come home with me so that we could test the helicopter out together. I can remember the excitement and the feeling of anticipation as if it were yesterday.

At half past three we practically ran all the way to my house. No one was in so we sat on the doorstep, waiting. Jack joined us and we threw stones at a coke can to pass the time. Right down the end of the street we could see dad's car coming home, driving slowly up the hill.

'He's coming! He's coming!' Billy yelled - for he was standing on the wall. 'I can see his car!'

My heart was pounding, the four of us all scrambled up to the gate and we waited. I hoped dad had the helicopter in the back of the car. I hoped he had put enough fuel in it - we had lots of flying to do. Dad pulled up outside and sat in the car, looking at us for a while, then slowly he heaved himself out. He had been drinking - he looked at us, four little boys, bright eyed, full of anticipation.

'What do you two boys want? Piss off home!' he snarled

at Billy and Robert. I could sense their discomfort - all our discomfort - as they shuffled their feet and looked down at the ground.

In a voice that seemed suddenly very small I said, 'They've come to see my helicopter.'

Dad just stared at me, scratched his head, he looked as if he had forgotten all about it, then he looked at me as if I were the most pathetic creature he had ever seen. Quite curtly he said, 'There's no bloody helicopter! Don't be such a stupid little kid. That's the trouble with you, Terry. You always take everything so bloody seriously. How could a silly little kid like you fly a helicopter about? For Christ's sake, boy! You, Billy Jones, Robert, you wouldn't believe something like that, would you? I bet you boys can take a wee joke!'

Then he sort of laughed awkwardly, struggled past us and let himself into the house. The door slammed shut.

We just stood there - Robert, Billy, Jack and me. I wanted the ground to open up and swallow me whole. Then I felt my eyes pricking and tears coming. I was going to cry - the shame of it! But not in front of my friends! Suddenly I was running, down the hill, across the road and into the park. I found a tiny hole in a hedge and climbed into it and sobbed and sobbed. I wanted to die - I never wanted to see anyone ever again.

What had happened? Why was I not getting my helicopter? What had gone wrong? Why had he said I was stupid? He had promised me a helicopter and I had believed him. What about Billy and Robert and lifts to school? Oh No! What about everyone else at school? What would they all say? Even Miss knew about my helicopter. She had smiled sweetly at me and said that not all dreams come true but I had told her - it was not a dream - it was true! I had been promised by my new dad!

As I sat there it all began to fall into place. Harry and his big stories - me a silly little kid. Harry having a thoroughly good time talking about all he was going to do for us - with our money. Harry was a liar. Harry was full of bullshit.

It was facing everyone at school again that was the hardest. An invisible steely shield sort of protected me from all the sneers and whispering. Robert found me at playtime and said it was a shame about the helicopter but his mum had known someone who had had one and it was useless - kept breaking down. After a few days it was never mentioned again and everyone forgot about it. But I did not forget. My invisible steely shield stayed with me after that and it protected me from bullies and from thugs - but mostly from Harry and all his bullshit.

One lunchtime, so drunk that he could hardly stand, Harry played cards in a pub with some men that he barely knew. He lost all the money he had on him and ended up signing away the ice cream van. A tall thin man picked it up the next day and the lad dad had employed to drive it lost his job instantly. Two weeks later in a similar incident dad was duped into signing an investment deal which later turned out to be the sale of the garage in Coatbridge for a minimal sum. Two men came round, probably for the deeds of the garage, and they sat in the living room with mum and Harry while we played with a toy on the floor. Mum screamed at them - they were sons of devils, they were sharks, they were the biggest pile of shit she had ever seen. One of the men just kept saying to calm it down, there was nothing she could do, it was all legal. After they went mum cried and shouted at Harry and he stormed out. In just over a fortnight he had lost everything for us and the £2000 was nearly gone.

Mum never liked the house at Chapelhall. Harry's wife had died there the year before and mum swore it was haunted. Early one morning she got up early. There had been a heavy drinking session the night before and she wanted a glass of water. At the top of the stairs she tripped and crashed down the entire flight, her head thudding against the front door at the bottom. There she stayed screaming out for help - her head against the door. Luckily Harry heard her cries and he appeared from the bedroom. Immediately he realised what had happened. In the lock of the front door was an enormous black key and mum had fallen straight on to it - the key had embedded itself into her eyebrow. Somehow Harry managed to pull the key out of the lock, mum still attached, screaming and crying out in pain. There she stood, a huge black key sticking out of her head, her thin body trembling uncontrollably, a little blood dribbling down her face.

Harry led her into the living room and sat her down. A neighbour came in and between them they managed to pull the key out. The neighbour kept running outside for handfuls of snow which she then put down mum's back! Jack said this must be to stop the flow of blood. Harry tore up a towel and wrapped mum's head up, she was unusually quiet and shook uncontrollably with the terror of it all. She was covered in blood from a very nasty wound. We were just glad that it was all nicely covered up now. No one suggested calling an ambulance or even getting a doctor to look at her. It seemed that we had all the first aid knowledge we could ever require right there in that front room. At least we knew how to prevent bleeding now - we just needed lots of snow!

Mum always swore blind that she was pushed down those stairs. It was the ghost of Harry's first wife who wanted us out, she maintained. To add to her argument one day Jack came running down the stairs insisting he could not open the bathroom door - something was leaning on it! We all dashed up there but it opened easily and we all burst in to the tiny bathroom. Harry's first wife had actually collapsed against the bathroom door when she had died and this added to mum's determination that the place was still occupied by her!

Just after Christmas 1961 Harry managed to single-handedly destroy our home. There was an open fire in the front room that needed cleaning out and lighting every morning. The fuel was provided free so we were never short of heat but our bunker leaked and the coal was often damp. One morning Jack and I sat together on the sofa watching Harry undergo the fire routine. He cursed as the coals would not light and we could see his short fuse getting shorter. We sat silently, hardly daring to move.

He stormed outside and after a few minutes returned with a milk bottle full of a clear liquid. He poured the contents onto the fire, whilst steadying himself on the mantelpiece. To our absolute horror, and so quickly that we would have missed it if we had blinked, flames began to lick up the petrol and into the bottle. Harry cried out and dropped it and flames suddenly shot out everywhere! Within seconds the rug was on fire, Harry kicked at the flames, trying frantically to stamp them out, but sparks shot out and hit the curtains, which quickly began to flare up. A thick smoke appeared from nowhere and we began to breathe in the putrid smell.

'Out! Out!' yelled Harry and Jack and I scrambled off the sofa and ran out after him into the cold morning air. We stood out there with him and mum appeared at the door, still in her night-clothes, pink swollen eyes, screaming abuse at him - 'What the bloody hell have you done? You bastard! You stupid fucking bastard!' We just stood there, coughing and spluttering, watching the flames inside the front room. Then the window burst and glass spears flew out everywhere. Neighbours appeared and we all watched as the house burnt.

A fire engine could be heard in the distance and we were led away with mum to a neighbouring house. We left Harry alone to watch as the firemen tackled his blaze. We had nowhere else to go so we had to move back into the house the next day - downstairs was black, wet and uninhabitable so we lived upstairs for a few days. It was cold and dark and smelt horrible. He really had lost us everything now.

Harry now decided that Scotland was the root of all evil and convinced mum that they should try their luck in England. There were no opportunities for families in Scotland, he said. London in the early sixties was the place to be and Harry wanted a slice of it. He wanted a new start, he wanted more cash.

In January 1962 we got onto the coach at Glasgow Coach

Station with seven bags of luggage and made the long journey to London Victoria for the first time. Just to keep them going mum had a bottle of sherry in her coat pocket and Harry-dad had a bottle of whisky. They had drunk the lot before we reached the border and slept the rest of the way. Jack and I sat huddled together, two small boys, leaving everything and everyone we had ever known, for a new life - in London.

Chapter 3

Harry seemed to secure accommodation for us with minimal problems. We all moved into an upstairs flat in a dead end street off Chiswick High Road. The houses were typical London Georgian buildings with railings at the front and they continued in long terraces. Two huge railway bridges crossed the road nearby and we would have to walk past many old tramps and down-and-outs who made their homes beneath the arches. They held their bottles and tins of drink in front of them and one old man had a big black pram full of old rubbish. I remembered that Angus had once been laid in a pram like that.....

Jack and I were quickly enrolled into a new school. It was incredibly strict and sadistic masters seemed to shout at the boys continually. I was absolutely terrified throughout the first week and longed for playtime when I could be with Jack. Moving to a new school is always a traumatic time to a certain extent but when you have a broad Scottish accent and no one can understand you it is even more difficult. Boys were caned across the knuckles for what seemed trivial offences and I always kept my hands out of sight incase a teacher rapped me just for the fun of it.

At playtime Jack and I began to notice groups of boys sitting together in a circle on the ground with others standing round them, cheering every now and then. Curiosity made us venture towards them but we could never quite see what was going on. One day a boy in Jack's class grinned at him and beckoned him over and we had our first glimpse from outside the circle at what the great attraction was.

It seemed that the cards from Brooke Bond tea packets was the current craze. Boys were winning them from each other in some sort of flicking game. The real champions had huge piles which they tied up with elastic bands at the end of play. These boys had status - they were the ones to be with - they were the in-crowd. I was never destined to be friends with them. I never even spoke to them. I do not think they knew I existed.

When one is a social outcast for whatever reason it makes sense to try and track down another and befriend him. And so it was that I started speaking to Arthur. Arthur Jenkins was a very strange boy. He wore odd clothes, was extremely thin and had one green eye and one blue. No one actually spoke to him or sat near him because he smelt, but when I first approached him he actually seemed to understand me and for the first time ever I began to take an interest in another boy besides Jack.

Arthur had a hobby. Brooke Bond tea cards were of no interest to him. He was far more concerned about tearing tiny strips of paper out of books without being caught. These he rolled into hard little balls and when they were of the right size he pushed them up his nostrils. When both nostrils were full of balls, somehow he would manage to produce an enormous sneeze and little white canon balls would shoot across the school room. Arthur would be triumphant if any hit the back of the boy two rows in front for that showed it had been a champion sneeze. I only tried it once but my sneeze did not come. I never knew what happened to the two balls I swear never came out.

Arthur had a big family - one of his brothers, a man really, would walk past the school occasionally with a scraggy little dog. He would talk to Arthur through the railings and the dog would wag its tail and lick him. Eventually I would join Arthur at the railings and the little dog would start to lick my hand too. How lovely it would be to have a pet.

****

Back home both mum and dad had employment now. He was working in a factory producing ball bearings and she was a waitress in a small cafe. When the school holidays came Jack and I spent hours wandering around Kensington Park until it was one o'clock. Then we would dash over to mum's cafe and she would dish us up sausage, egg and chips. We had to eat it quickly and get out - the owner only had half an hour or so for his lunch and mum did not want him to see us. I wonder if he ever noticed how much of his profits went in to our stomachs!

After we had eaten it was back to the park for another hour or so until mum finished work. Then the three of us would walk home together. She talked to us sometimes. She did not like Chiswick, she missed Scotland and she was fed up with Harry. Generally they were drinking more and more and weekends were one long booze-up. Jack and I became quite self-reliant. We had gone through the stage where we were absolutely terrified as soon as they raised their voices. Now we were resigned to accepting it all as part of the course of life - maybe this was normal life for everyone. Dad was happy to surround himself with bottles and drink his way slowly to oblivion. Mum fiercely denied ever having touched a drop, but her supplies were hidden round the flat!

Sometimes dad was sober for a couple of weeks at a time and during these times he would take us out for walks and play at being an ideal father. On one of these outings he met a Polish man and got into conversation with him while Jack and I played on the swings. A week later we were on the move again - to a house in Ladbroke Grove, Notting Hill. Now we were in a basement flat of a terraced house. We walked down stone steps with railings, then we turned back on ourselves to go in the front door. This was a bigger flat than our last one. There was a living room at the front and beyond that a long corridor with doors off it. We had a kitchen and two bedrooms. The Polish man was the landlord and he lived upstairs with an assortment of relatives.

Almost immediately dad sub-let one of the bedrooms to two Irish lads. One of them was quite friendly and would send Jack and me out for his shopping - always the same order - a pint of milk and a packet of fig rolls. When we delivered them to him he would open the biscuits and give us one each.

'I wish we had a pet,' I said to dad as we walked through Portobello Road market one Saturday morning. 'I'd love a little dog.' Dad was not at all keen on having a dog and he changed the subject immediately.

We stopped at a stall and Jack and I admired a beautiful model battleship. It had been painstakingly put together by someone, then painted and now it was mounted on a stand and up for sale. Dad saw us looking at it and later as we wandered off down through the market we glanced round and saw he had it under his arm! Many years before he had been in the Navy and I think he suddenly felt a blast from the past when he saw that battleship. Needless to say it was useless as a toy to Jack and me and within days we had destroyed it.

Every other day Jack and I would loiter as the stall holders packed up, then along with many other young children, we would rush around picking up fruit and vegetables that had been discarded or had rolled into the gutter. It was a wonderful way to get free food and the only way mum could afford to feed us anything reasonably fresh!

Portobello Road market with its vivid collection of sights and smells and noise, was dad's favourite haunt and often he came home after a few drinks with more absolutely useless bits and pieces under his arm. Invariably mum would lose her temper with him over the waste of money, never more so than when he appeared back with Sammy.

We were sitting watching our tiny television one Saturday evening when we heard dad open the front door. In he came triumphantly with a little thin Capuchin monkey sitting on his shoulder. It had a collar on with a long chain and wore a red waistcoat and a little pointed hat with a bell on it. As we stared in absolute astonishment, it began leaping from one of dad's shoulders to another. He struggled to control it as he said, slightly slurred: 'Here you are Terry, you wanted a pet, have a monkey!' He peeled it from his back and dropped it in front of me.

Mum screamed and shouted at him, then at me and grabbing her coat she stormed out in a temper. Jack and I led the monkey by its little lead gingerly into the bedroom. We had no idea what to do with it. What did monkeys eat?

'Why do you want a monkey?' asked Jack.

'I don't - I wanted a dog or a cat.'

We watched as it climbed over the beds and sat on a chest of drawers. It looked at us with round beady eyes, then opened its mouth wide in a sort of yawn. It had the most enormous white teeth. It looked almost comical in its little red clothes and the bell tinkled every time it moved. I decided that was to warn you it was coming your way so you had time to take cover from those enormous vampire teeth!

That evening Jack and I took Sammy the monkey out for a walk in the park on his chain. It was dusk and quite chilly but we wanted him to eat some leaves or something before bed time. Jack decided he probably needed a run off the lead, like people do with their dogs, so I undid his little collar, let him trot off and we never saw him again. We walked around for hours looking for Sammy and calling for him. Every now and then we could hear a shrill scream in the distance but I never knew if it was Sammy screaming or someone he was terrorising with those huge teeth!

After a lifetime in captivity, Sammy finally had his freedom. I often thought of him and could imagine him ripping off his little clothes as he scampered up a tree in Kensington Gardens. I had had a pet for less than a day.

****

The two Paddys, as dad called them, were our lodgers for quite a few months. They were only young boys really and they had labouring jobs quite close by. Their room was bleak and they shared a double bed - their few possessions littered the entire room, uneaten food was lying around amongst grubby work clothes and foul smelling socks. They spent a lot of time talking about girls and who they wanted to spend a night with, but we were never aware that either of them ever had a girlfriend.

When dad went in to wake them for work on a Monday morning there were many more than four feet sticking out the end of that bed and he evicted them there and then. They managed to get all their possessions and six mates out onto the street in less than ten minutes. Jack and I were sad to see them go for they had always been kind to us and were better than no one to have around when mum and dad were out drinking.

Mum and dad argued and fought so much and although Jack and I hated it, our resiliency increased. Perhaps everyone's parents behaved truculently behind closed doors - we knew no better then and there were no alternatives anyway. We knew how to make ourselves scarce though. Dad could be very aggressive with us if we got in the way at the wrong time. So it was strange that there was a period of icy silence between them during the autumn months. I could not understand what the problem was but it was something to do with dad's regular visits to a clinic and something I thought I heard mum call 'VP.'

I begged mum to tell me what VP was and eventually (she could never keep a secret anyway after a few drinks) she spat it out - you caught it from dirty women! My imagination went into overdrive. It was a very long time before I understood the veracity of the matter. All I knew at the time was that VP sherry was sold in the off-licence and it was something to do with dirty women. It was all very confusing and very worrying, especially when mum drank it!

Christmas 1962 was a great excuse for partying. Jack and I spent most of the time on our own in our bleak rooms. There was no roast turkey for us. We wandered through the streets of London peering into shop windows, looking at all the bright lights and the beautiful gifts for sale. We watched televisions churning out Christmas programmes inside the electrical shop windows and we stood outside glittery tinsel adorned toy shops looking at all the cars and action men for sale. We saw parents buying huge quantities of presents for their children and wondered if dad was buying anything for us. Everywhere was sparkling and exciting and excessive. Best of all, Jack and I would stand outside the bakery - the cake shop and just absorb the delicious smells. Once or twice we just had enough money to buy a small cake which we tore into two and shared. I can remember Jack dropping his half once and in his dismay, he grappled on the pavement, picking it all up before dusting it down and eating it anyway. I always loved the thought of Christmas, I loved the lights and the glamour, but it was never for us. We were only ever spectators.

Dad had made enormous quantities of barley soup before Christmas and we heated that up for our dinner. It was greasy and lumpy and I spent ages picking out the lumps of congealed barley. Dad would have given me a real thrashing if he could have seen me! Jack invented soup sandwiches! I was glad dad was not there.

On New Year's Day in the afternoon, mum and dad brought friends back when they came home. Mr and Mrs Green seemed quite sober in comparison with our parents and they made polite conversation with us while dad rummaged around for clean glasses. Everyone was chatting amiably at first but gradually as they became more intoxicated, so they became more aggressive. Mum was going on and on, swearing, provoking, annoying everyone. From the initial happy Christmas scene, the situation quickly deteriorated into mum against the world. Her tongue really was her worst enemy!

Dad stood up, glass in hand and spat at her to shut up. She looked up at him from her arm chair. 'And what are you going to do about it if I don't?' she smirked. 'Hit me again? Well, go on then - hit me!' Dad turned away, Jack and I could see he was fuming but all would be all right if only mum kept quiet. The other couple fell strangely silent and the man looked at his watch.

'You bastard!' mum said, totally confident that she was safe in front of visitors. 'You do nothing for me, you bastard. You're a laughing stock, a waster. You don't like the truth, do you? Listen to me, you fucking bastard!.....'

In one swift movement, practised so many times, dad turned, walked over to her and punched her in the face, so hard that it knocked her and the chair backwards. She staggered up, screaming, blood pouring from her nose.

'My nose! You bastard! You've broken my fucking nose!' she screamed.

Mr and Mrs Green were rooted to the spot for a second or two. They had never been so embarrassed in their lives. As dad went back to have another go at mum they managed to get up and disappear out the front door. Jack and I quickly followed them and sat on the steps outside while the punch-up continued. Mum tried to follow us and made a desperate lunge for the front door, but dad grabbed her and turned her round so that she was facing him. Holding her shoulder he positioned himself for a thunderous punch, but as he punched she ducked and he missed her face and hit the door. He totally smashed his knuckle on that huge oak door but he did not feel a thing. Jack and I sat outside, listening - yelling and shouting, things being smashed, neighbours calling out to them to shut up......
Then dad appeared at the steps, mum's blood on his white shirt, his blood dripping from his right hand and he staggered off up the road, cursing her as he went.

Jack and I crept back inside. It was as if a bomb had gone

off in there and mum was lying semi-conscious on the floor. The Polish man appeared, he took one look at her and called for an ambulance. Minutes later she was carried away on a stretcher and rushed to hospital and Jack and I did our best to clear up the mess. Shortly after that the police arrived and arrested dad (who was sitting up the road) and the Polish man took charge of us that night. His wife fed us and put us to bed.

At lunchtime the next day dad came back. He had appeared in the magistrates court and been released. Mum was in hospital for three days and when she came home she let it be known that Harry was nothing but the devil in disguise. No one could have had more venomous thoughts towards him than she and she made his life a living hell.

Dad plunged himself into an orgy of drink. He lost his job and sank deep into depression. He befriended a bunch of criminals who lived up the road and seemed to make money by looking after stolen goods for them - this kept us from starvation. But he was really only bothered about having enough alcohol and one evening with no money, the easiest way to get a drink was to steal it. So he threw a brick through the window of an off-licence, reached inside and helped himself to three bottles, then settled down on a park bench with the one and only aim of becoming as drunk as possible.

When the police arrested him he was so intoxicated that they had to drag him across the park to the waiting car. He left them two presents - an evil smelling wet patch on the back seat and a pile of alcoholic vomit on the floor.

At about the time Kennedy was assassinated, our dad was being assassinated in court. He got six months for robbery and began a stretch in Wormwood Scrubs. We visited him once, two small boys and their mother. He was so remorseful, so full of plans for when he came home. Life was going to be great for us in the future and we were just to hang on for him.

'I've always loved you, Alice,' he said, trying to take her hand, which she pulled stiffly away. 'And I'm sorry about all this - I'll make it up to you when I get out.'

But it was too late. Mum had had enough. She was leaving him. We were going back to Scotland.

As we climbed into a taxi in Ladbroke Grove, two brightly dressed Jamaican women were fighting on the pavement. One had her shoe in her hand and was plunging the heel into the other one's head - there was blood everywhere. I was so pleased that it was all over for us, finally, at last, Harry was gone and there would be peace. Mum would be fine now without him, there was just no doubt about that at all. We travelled back to Glasgow overnight and Uncle Jim met us at the coach station.

Chapter 4

For a short while we stayed on the Easterhouse estate just outside Glasgow, with Uncle Jim and his new wife Aunt Barbara. They had a baby boy of their own and for the first time in ages Jack and I mentioned Angus. He would be four years old now and we wondered what he looked like. Mum had a picture of him aged two with his gran, but we guessed he must have changed a bit.

Mum and Aunt Barbara fought like cat and dog. They were both strong-minded Glasgow women and each was wildly jealous of the other. Before we knew it they wanted us out and mum decided we should stay with her oldest brother who lived in Penicuik, near Edinburgh. She had the offer of a job in Inverness. It was hotel work and she was good at that, she said. She would be back for us in six month's time.

Jack and I met Uncle Don for the first time in December 1963. Mum said she was sorry she could not be with us for Christmas but she needed the money and the hotel was paying extra over the festive season. Jack and I clung to her as she prised herself away towards the waiting taxi. We both wanted her to stay but she insisted this was for the best. Uncle Don took us inside but I glanced round once and I swear I saw her wipe a tear away as she watched us from the back of the taxi.

Uncle Don was married to an English woman, Cathy from Coventry. They were a much older couple who had raised two children successfully. They had broken away from the rest of the family in Glasgow, and, whether because of this, or because of any other reason, they were stable, good and kind.

Cathy was a lovely woman and she did her very best to make us feel at home. We lapped up all the love and attention and they were the happiest days we had ever had.

Uncle Don was a postman and he promised us trips in his post van as soon as he could. Christmas was wonderful. We had presents under a Christmas tree and a lovely turkey roast dinner. Jack and I were thrilled and surprised by it all. Uncle Don's children were both there for Christmas Day and the daughter, who was a ballerina, hugged me and cut Jack's hair for him. We laughed and played games and were warm and happy.

Aunt Cathy took us out and bought us new clothes. She insisted we had outgrown some of the things we had and also we needed uniform for the new school we were to attend. No expense seemed to be spared. School was extremely strict - marching around the playground and saluting the teachers featured strongly, but because we were so happy we did not mind. Aunt Cathy was always at the school gates at three thirty to walk us home from school and she held our hands and chatted to us in a facultative way. We never heard a cross word in all the time we were there. The house was quite large and down the end of the garden was a chicken house. Every morning before school Jack and I would delve around in the hen house searching for eggs which we would then proudly produce to Aunt Cathy as if we had laid them ourselves! In the evening we would scatter corn for them. One of the hens only had one wing and we liked her best. Secretly, she was my pet.

Uncle Don could not wait to take us out in his van. He was the original Postman Pat and he would drive miles across the Scottish wilderness to deliver post to remote farms. Jack and I had a wonderful time, although it was totally against the rules for us to travel with him. When Uncle Don arrived back at the depot Jack and I would hide inside the big mail sacks with the tie tops drawn tight. Uncle Don would collect the next sack of mail and once safely away Jack and I would emerge and laugh and scream with excitement that we had not been caught. It was the most exciting adventure!

On a lovely Spring day there was a fancy dress party in the local park. Aunt Cathy suddenly produced two costumes that she had been labouring over for weeks. Jack and I were to go as Fred Flintstone and Barney Rubble! There was a fair there too and we rode on nearly everything. It was a brilliant day.

When it finally drew to an end Uncle Don and Aunt Cathy started walking home, Jack and I trailing behind, still clutching a tube of sweets each, laughing and chatting about our day.

As we crossed the road a car appeared from nowhere, someone screamed out and as I looked up the car hit me and tossed me up and over and I landed with a heavy thud on the path. It was a Hillman Minx and the driver, an elderly man, was beside himself with remorse. He had not seen me, I had appeared from nowhere, he had only looked down for a second......

A crowd was gathering around me quickly. 'Don't move,' people were saying. 'Wait for the ambulance.'

Aunt Cathy knelt beside me, real concern etched into her kind face. 'Does anything hurt, Terry?' she asked in a quiet gentle voice.

'My leg.'

'Don't move, then,' she said. 'It'll be all right.'

With that I managed to struggle up, stand up straight and then very carefully walk away, much to everyone's amazement. With his very bravest face on, Barney Rubble walked home with Fred Flintstone and told everyone he was fine. The most spectacular bruise came up and it hurt like hell. I could not bare anyone to touch it for ages but I never told Aunt Cathy the pain I was in. I did not want anything to spoil all the happy times we were having.

On Sports Day Uncle Don and Aunt Cathy were there to see me win the 50 yard race, the sack race and I jumped the highest out of our whole year. I had a little trophy for the most promising junior sportsman and I was bursting with pride. Aunt

Cathy framed my certificate and even rang her daughter up to say how well I had done. Uncle Don gave me a shilling to spend as I wanted. They could not have been prouder if I had been their own son. Jack was quite envious. I had never felt so important.

We started going to chapel again. Jack and I went to confirmation classes and we really felt like good Catholic boys. I prayed to God that I was sorry I did not speak to him anymore but a lot had happened and I had not meant to forget him. I got into the practice of saying Hail Mary's to myself all the way to and from chapel and I really felt my soul being cleansed. It seemed that all would be fine now. We just had to trust in the Lord and everything would be perfect. He would always be there for us, always caring for us. Our Father would never let us down.

> *'Dear God, thank you for the home where we live,*
> *Thank you for your love and care for all the people in*
> *   your family,*
> *I belong to your family, make me full of love too,*
> *Please let us stay in Penicuik forever*
> *And please look after Sammy and mum.'*

I did not know why Our Father did not hear my prayers - maybe he was busy or maybe we were just too undeserving, but of course, it all came to an end at Penicuik one beautiful sunny day in July 1964. Uncle Don wrote to mum asking if he and Cathy could adopt us. He explained how happy we were, how good the school was and they had plenty of room and plenty of money. We too wanted to stay, he said. Please could she consider it and of course she could visit whenever she wanted.

Within four days mum was on the doorstep, absolutely furious. Jack and I had to leave school early and when we got home Aunt Cathy was crying as she packed our bags. She told us we were lovely boys and she hoped we would visit whenever we could. She really hoped she would see us again soon. We were pleased to see mum but could not understand quite what was going on. She was so angry she hardly spoke to us. We heard her shout at Don that she had trusted him and he had betrayed her - that nothing and no one would every make her give her boys up.

'I've already lost one,' she cried. 'I will never give up my two boys and YOU should have known better!'

'Alice, Alice,' we heard him saying in his gentle, even voice, 'I only had the boys' interests at heart. I never knew it would upset you so much - there's really no need for all this fuss...'

'Fuss? I don't call this fuss! I call this **you** trying to steal my boys! My Boys! They belong with their mother! You and your posh ways! Always thinking you know best - bloody Cathy and her posh ways - how dare you try and steal my boys!'

Uncle Don and Aunt Cathy both kissed and hugged us as our belongings were piled into a taxi. I began to cry uncontrollably at the thought of leaving them and Jack was crying too. Mum said she would be in touch. Aunt Cathy had the reddest eyes I had ever seen. Mum was so angry that they had dared to try and keep us permanently that she never visited them again. Indeed, I did not see them again for twenty years.

Technically we were a homeless family. Mum took us into central Glasgow and after two nights camping outside an official building with mum shouting at various people inside, we were handed the keys of an apartment. Mum was triumphant that she had secured a place for us and we trudged along to find our new address - 63 Mansion Street.

It was an aptly named place, was Mansion Street - right in the middle of the Gorbols, arguably the most notorious estate in Europe. Window after window in a dirty grey tenement building, five stories high, that went on for the length of a whole street. We had two dirty, damp, squalid rooms with some stained furniture left behind by the previous occupants. A filthy cooker in the kitchen was yellow and congealed with many years of grease. A butler sink had a permanently dripping tap that had stained it yellow. Out of the windows we could see across the roof-tops of Glasgow. There was a small Formica table in the kitchen with two chairs.

The main room doubled up as the bedroom. Besides the stained sofa there were two mattresses on the floor. Surprisingly they did not appear too damp and mum unpacked her bag and produced some blankets. She made up a bed for us to share - we did not undress, just climbed into it and lay together, listening to mum scrubbing in the kitchen, her sleeves rolled up, her fair hair flopping about as she worked. One bare light bulb swung from the ceiling, lighting the room bleakly. I think we were numb with anticipation as we drifted off into uneasy sleep.

In the morning Jack and I could look round and explore our new home. It was certainly tatty but mum had tried her best to clean it up. We had a long walk down a corridor to the toilets which we could smell from thirty paces. Quite often there was a regular occupant of the first toilet - an old woman, who would spend hours just sitting there with her knickers round her ankles. She had a dark overcoat on and as she swigged from a bottle she sang sad dreary songs. Sometime she called out to Jack and me to join her. We would run like bats out of hell!

The tenement buildings had been built in one huge square and enclosed in the 'yard' in the centre were what looked like brick air raid shelters which were separated by many dustbins. Jack and I spent a lot of time jumping from the roofs on to the bins, which swarmed with rats. The days were long and hot which meant we had loads of time to explore the place. We were two boys aged eight and ten and we could have been just ripe to be initiated into a local gang.

The dominant local gang was the Baileys - the vast majority of them came from the Bailey family, a real rough lot. The youngest boy was six, the eldest, who was a cousin of the Baileys, was fourteen. They were Glasgow's rejects - the toughest, meanest, most lawless kids we had ever met. They were full of hate. As far as they could see they ruled the Gorbols and would march down the centre of the streets throwing stones and bottles at anything remotely interesting or even that moved. They quickly attacked any parked car, removing wheels and smashing windows, therefore the whole place was a scrap heap of car parts. Jack and I were absolutely terrified of them all but quickly realised that we would have to appear to befriend them, just for safety's sake.

After we had lived in Mansion Street for a few days two of the Baileys approached us, cornered us by some bins and roughed us up a bit. A boy not any taller than Jack held a broken bottle at my throat and warned me that if they saw us wandering about 'their patch' there could be a big problem. Jack and I knew what they meant - although we insisted we would never cross them it seemed to fall on deaf ears and we ran back home as fast as we could. Now every time we went out we had to check the coast was clear. Encounters with the Baileys were to be avoided at all costs.

The older boys in the gang had vicious looking penknives and a dagger, but for the smaller boys, improvisation was the name of the game. They painstakingly tied razor blades to the end of lolly sticks and used these for the most appalling crimes.

Gerald, the leader, had furry balls hanging on his belt. Every now and then someone would present him with a few more which he would carefully thread string through before attaching to his belt. I often wondered what they were. We just watched the goings on from afar.

One day I got a letter. It was from Uncle Don and Aunt Cathy and folded neatly inside was a small newspaper cutting. There was a picture of me holding a little trophy and underneath it said, 'Terry Steer - the most promising junior sportsman, 1964.' For some inexplicable reason I began to cry. Jack came and had a look and said it was a shame I did not have the trophy still. I said I did, mum had it safe for me. But secretly I knew I had not seen it since we left Uncle Don's and realistically, I did not ever expect to see it again. I put my newspaper cutting back in my letter and tucked them under my pillow. I would show mum when she came home - she would be so proud....

Even the animal world in the Gorbols was devoid of affection, or even tolerance of each other and the instinctive crudity in their behaviour seemed sadly ominous. One evening Jack and I watched as two terrier dogs fought wildly in the street, ripping each other apart in the most ferocious fight I had ever seen. A man appeared and smashed them over the heads with a spade. One yelped and staggered off, the other dog lay twitching on the road. The man smashed it over the head again and I think it died.

Later one of the boys in the Bailey gang could be seen struggling with something in the back yard around the bins. Once we were sure that he was on his own Jack and I went over to see what was going on and were horrified to see him hanging a cat by its neck. The poor thing was jerking wildly and emitting gurgling noises. Before we could do anything the boy sliced the cat's paws off roughly with his lolly stick weapon. Blood poured from the poor animal. We could hardly bear to watch as it died. The boy put the four paws into his pocket, scowled at us, then disappeared.

Next day Gerald had four more furry balls on his belt and the boy, probably younger than us, had five cigarettes to smoke. This was a mean, grim, dangerous place where we lived on a knife edge. Just a look at the wrong person or in the wrong direction could mean getting attacked so we permanently kept our heads down. Both Jack and I wished we could stop feeling so scared.

Acceptance into the Baileys gang seemed almost impossible - we could never kill a cat or cause a poor animal pain so Jack and I always seemed to be on the outside, looking in, always scared of being picked on or bullied, always looking out, checking that we would be safe. It was mum, strangely enough, who put us out of danger. She had a new boyfriend. He was Gerald senior, father of Gerald Cat Paws.

Gerald senior thought he was a pretty tough guy. His wife had died and he had brought Gerald Cat Paws up for the past ten years. He was pretty satisfied with his talents as a father and felt his success was due to his belt and the fact that Gerald had not attended school since he was eleven: 'There's nothing a school can teach that boy that I can't better,' he was fond of saying.

Jack and I nearly dropped dead with fright when we arrived home for tea one evening to see the two Geralds sitting in our room. Although he did not acknowledge us then, Gerald Cat Paws was always all right with us after that. He stopped sneering at us and almost looked out for us in his own odd way. All the other boys in the gang stopped scowling at us too, and occasionally one of them would nod in reluctant acknowledgement from the other side of the street. They did not want us in their gang but at least they had stopped threatening us.

Gerald senior never actually moved in with us but he was with mum a lot of the time. He did not seem to work - well not legitimately anyway, and often we would see him dish out money to mum. She did not seem to work now either. A lot of the time was spent drinking and talking about Harry. She really went on about Harry a lot. Gerald senior heard all about her beatings, the abuse, the violence, the drinking. Yes, it was all Harry's fault, she said, all her misfortune was due to Harry. As soon as she could sort it out she was divorcing the bastard. Gerald senior said all the things she wanted to hear. She had him now, he would never desert her, he was a force to be reckoned with. He had mates who would help him reduce Harry to a pulp. Harry had better never show his ugly face round there. Why he, Gerald, had murdered at least three men who had done less than Harry. Harry would be mincemeat if he ever showed up.

Jack and I would look at each other and wonder what sort of method Gerald would use in his extermination of Harry. Jack said he hoped Harry never showed up and met Gerald - he did not want to see the fight.

I had a new pet. A pigeon had started visiting us and Jack and I would put crumbs on the window-sill outside and watch as 'our' pigeon came and pecked at them. After a while Pigeon started pecking the glass first thing in the morning and we would open the window and put out our few crumbs for him. I really grew to love Pigeon.

We shared our rooms with a few other animals too. At night cockroaches appeared, scuttling around and over our beds on the floor. One crawled over my face once and I screamed for ages. Besides the 'roaches were a couple of mice which could be seen racing round the edge of the room at night in their never ending search for food. And of course, outside in the yard there were armies of rats. The rats attracted cats from far and wide and the cats kept Gerald's belt thick and bulky.

It was morning - tap, tap, tap....on the window. Pigeon was there, his little head bobbing up and down. I opened the window a little,

'Hang on there, wee Pigeon,' I said. 'I'll just get your bread...'

As I turned to go to the kitchen there was an almighty bang and Pigeon blew up in a cloud of feathers. I stared in disbelief and shock as feathers flew around, settling on the blood splattered window-sill.

'What the hell's happened?' blurted Jack sleepily from the floor.

'Pigeon exploded,' I said. But I had no idea what had happened.

It was only later that I overheard Gerald Cat Paws telling someone that his mate had shot a pigeon with an air rifle that morning. It had been a perfect hit and he had won five shillings. He lived in the tenement building directly opposite us. I was really sad. Pigeon had trusted us and we had partly caused his death.

We had to go to school in central Glasgow - a school that was opposite a crematorium which was quite unusual then.

Every couple of days there would be a funeral there and afterwards the chimney would emit wispy brown smoke. The smell of burning bodies became very familiar to us and unfortunately always reminded me of lunchtime!

On my ninth birthday it was Gerald senior who gave me a present - a bag of balloons. Jack and I blew them all up and sold them for a penny each. Then we bought a few penny sweets.

Mum was definitely not drinking quite so much now. She still drank at weekends and most evenings she would have a drink, but generally there were no bottles hidden in cupboards and we were getting regular meals. Gerald senior brought drink up to the rooms and they would sit and watch television together. She shouted at him quite a bit but he did not retaliate the way Harry did. He was quite a quiet, gentle man really - except when Harry was mentioned, then he would launch himself into the 'What I'll do to that man you'll never know,' speeches and we would all yawn and switch off.

A knock at the door one evening was quite unusual. Gerald got up to answer it.

'And who are you?' we heard him say.

'Who are you?' was the reply. Jack and I pricked our ears up.

Gerald puffed himself up. 'Look mate, who the fuck are you?'

'Harry' came a familiar voice - Jack and I exchanged glances - so this was it then, the Big Fight that had been talked about and planned for so long. The moment had come!

Gerald was silent for one second, then he turned, grabbed his coat, pushed past Harry and was down the corridor and down five flights of stone stairs before we could even blink. For all his tough words Gerald senior was the biggest coward we had ever met. Harry strolled into the room.

'And who was he?' he chuckled. Then, 'Hullo Alice, hullo boys, I'm home!'

Harry had been released from prison quite some time before

and had been living in Surrey. Now he had come back for his family. He wanted us to all move to England again with him. He had some money, he said, and he was brimming over with new ideas. He thought he had convinced mum to join him. She was living in a stinking shit hole and life was rosy down south. Harry stayed a week, then left to find us somewhere to live in England. We found out later that he walked nearly all the way from Glasgow to Surrey!

After he had gone mum assured us we were not going anywhere with him and she immediately gave up the apartment. We thought at the time she was trying to hide from Harry but it was probably only because the rent was due and she could not pay it now that Gerald had vanished. We had lived in the Gorbols for one whole year. We had been frozen and hungry in the long winter months, continually frightened and miserable - bullied at school and left to run wild at home. But we had learnt to survive. If we could survive there we could survive anything.

****

Mum literally had nowhere to go. She decided the time was right to make a visit.

We arrived at our Gran's house one sunny morning and walked in on Angus having lunch with her. He was six years old and lived in an Aladdin's cave of toys and beautiful things. We were surprised that we had no feelings for him at all. He was a stranger living with our Gran and she indulged him and pampered him as she had never done her own children. We touched his precious belongings, we tried to find out how things worked, how they had been put together and he squealed at us in dismay as wheels fell off in our hands and Action Man heads snapped and broke. Gran was furious with us. She roughly pushed us out of Angus's grotto and locked the door.

Jack and I sat on the sofa and watched plump little Angus as he was spoon fed and had his fair hair combed. Gran put a little kilt on him and he danced to Scottish music! What a stupid kid! We had to clap along to the music and mum laughed and sang! We did not like Angus very much. After a whole day with them, mum decided we had to go and we were deposited at Uncle Jim's for the night. Mum actually went back to Gran's where she stayed for two weeks. Gran could only put up with her for that long as she was drunk the whole time. She fell in a ditch full of mud and nearly drowned and she kept bringing home an assortment of friends after the pubs shut. It was extremely upsetting for Angus who was terrified of her.

Uncle Jim wanted us out too. He had a second child now and did not have the room for us. He phoned mum and told her he was going to arrange for us to go into care. She must have contacted Harry somehow because shortly after we found ourselves all packed up and on the move again. It was Harry's trump card. He always insisted he would never let her boys go into care and she was reassured by this. We travelled back to England on the overnight coach in August 1965 and listened to Beatles songs on a transistor radio. Mum said she would follow as soon as she could. She had a few things to do first.

Harry was waiting for us at Victoria.

Chapter 5

H arry had spent quite some time in the station bar and was reasonably merry when he spotted us. We were just relieved to see a familiar face. He rushed us round to a platform at the train station and we caught a train to Dorking in Surrey. After a quick stop at a pub we caught a bus to Newdigate, a beautiful village in the middle of nowhere. We climbed off the bus at four in the afternoon, absolutely exhausted, thinking we were at our new home. Harry announced there was now a three mile walk! Jack and I trudged along with our bags, practically asleep on our feet.

Harry did not want us to miss a thing in this wonderful new place that he had chosen for us. There were fields everywhere - cows and sheep, people riding along cheerfully on bicycles, trees and birds... everything country life was supposed to be. As dusk fell we still had a long way to go. We could barely keep our eyes open.

The sun was very low in the sky now, my arms were aching so much I thought I was just going to have to stop. Harry suddenly turned us up a rough, cobbled unmade road and we struggled along for half a mile or so. I saw a glow-worm in the hedge and gnats and mosquitoes buzzed round our heads. We crossed a cattle grid and suddenly in front of us were caravans. In the remaining evening light we could see them clearly, some with lights on inside and little curtains drawn.

'Here we are boys - our one is number nine!' Harry said proudly. He had a fresh spring in his step as he approached a caravan set back in the darkness from all the others. We followed wide-eyed, Harry opened the door and switched on a light. We stepped up and into the brightness. It was a basic holiday caravan really, built-in seating and wardrobes, a bed that pulled down from the wall, a tiny kitchen and miniature sink. Harry had a pot of cold barley soup on the cooker.

'Come on boys,' he said as he lit a match to heat it up. 'Have some soup, then bed.' For a second I panicked. Jack and I exchanged worried glances, then I was reassured by remembering I had four pockets on me as long as I kept my coat on!

After we had eaten dad started making up our beds. He directed us to the toilets in a block opposite and behind there I emptied my pockets of barley soup - disgusting greasy stuff. How could Jack eat it? Maybe Jack was just so hungry. We were full of plans to explore and decided it would be the first thing we would do in the morning. We slept like logs for fourteen hours.

When I woke up I could see the morning sun had sliced in through the cracks in the curtains and lay in bright lines across our beds. I lay quite still, listening to the new sounds - birds singing, gentle voices in the very far distance. I glanced across at Jack and as he was awake too we quickly got up and dressed. We trotted through to the kitchen where dad had left two boiled eggs for us in egg cups. We could hardly believe our luck - he must have left them for us before he went to work. As soon as we had eaten them we opened the door and the sun streamed in on us, warming our faces in a way we had never felt before. First impressions, those very important first impressions, often stay with you for life and these etched their way onto my memory for ever.

We were stepping into a beautiful new world. There was a magnificent blue sky on this late summer's day and all around us were assorted fruit trees - apples, pears, plums, all ripe and ready for picking. The caravans had neatly laid out gardens around them, gnomes fished in ponds and forks and spades lay idly against a fence. It was all so colourful, so peaceful. No dustbins overflowing with putrid rubbish, no rats scampering about at the slightest disturbance, no tortured animals laying dying... nothing like Glasgow at all. This place was just a mass of colour and the overwhelming smell was of freshly mown grass. It was all so clean and bright that we felt as if angels had come and lifted us into heaven. I do not think I had ever seen an apple tree before and I walked over and plucked one. Absolutely delicious!

My eyes almost hurt from taking in all the colour around us. This was such a strange new world but what a calm and peaceful one. Did people really live here all the time in such tranquillity? No shouting, no town noises at all...just birds singing.

Jack and I followed the path round past all the caravans until we reached the cattle grid that we had clambered over awkwardly the night before. This marked the entrance to the site and over to the right we could see old people dressed in white, playing bowls on a bowling green which looked as if it were carpeted in lush dark green grass. We wandered over to watch as they rolled their black balls slowly along, chatting amiably and laughing with delight occasionally. It was all very slow, very friendly, very peaceful.

Jack and I, raw Glasgow boys, wandered back to the fruit trees and plucked plums and apples. Jack ran back to get a saucepan so we could fill it up with fruit for later. We spent all afternoon eating fruit, sitting on the grass outside our caravan, dozing in the sun and by five o'clock we were absolutely bloated. Suddenly dad appeared. He was riding a bicycle! He had obviously cycled home from work and he was red faced, puffing, but looked exhilarated.

'Hullo boys!' he said as he dismounted. 'How have you enjoyed your day?'

We told him all about the fruit trees and the old people playing bowls as he cooked our tea. Jack and I were not hungry, in fact we both felt sick. Dad suggested we go easy on the fruit but we did not think such lovely delicious fruit could make you ill.

The next day we were off to explore again. Now we noticed that our caravan was quite different from all the others. It was much older and tattier, scruffy pale blue paintwork with a darker blue band round the middle. It was rounded in shape while all the others were rectangular. Most of the caravans seemed to be permanently fixed in place with their neat tended gardens round them, but ours seemed to have been abandoned on a piece of spare land at the end. There were not even proper steps going up to it - just an upturned orange crate. Still, none of that mattered when you lived in paradise!

By the third day Jack and I were ill. Almost every twenty minutes we made a dash for the toilets and we became a very familiar sight in the shower block! We had never been so clean. But the showers were a real novelty.

On the Saturday dad did not go to work but when he popped out, Jack and I took the opportunity to play on his bike. We rode it around crazily, we crashed into trees, bent the handlebars back the wrong way, charged down the bumpy lane outside the park, two up - yes, we went mad that Saturday and we totally wrecked dad's bike.

When dad appeared back and saw the mangled heap that had once been his bike he was absolutely furious. He held each of us in turn while he hit us with his enormous hands. Lying in bed that night, tired and bruised, we grinned and decided it had been worth it. We had never been on a bike before.

Mum appeared a few days later, in a taxi. She generally cleaned up the caravan and gave it a woman's touch. It was really home now. The next day they went shopping and presented us with a decorative jug full of Merrydown cider that they had bought for us. They were going up the pub now and the cider was our treat for the evening. In Scotland cider was a non-alcoholic drink similar to lemonade, but in England it was very potent. Jack and I sat down in front of the television with our enormous jug and drank glass after glass!

After a while I began to feel decidedly strange. When I needed to answer nature's inevitable call I found myself staggering out and on the ground - somehow I had fallen down the step. But it did not matter, it did not seem to hurt at all. But why were there two toilet blocks now? Which one should I head for? I was well and truly intoxicated and two hours later I was as sick as a dog. We slept well again that night, Jack and I....both on the floor under the table. Mum and dad were not in a much better state when they came in but they managed to lift us up onto our beds.

Very quickly we settled in. We started new schools in September - the Newdigate Village School for me, but because Jack was now eleven, he had to go to the senior school some way away in Beare Green. The other children were not impressed with me at all. Again, they could not understand my raw accent and I was quickly nicknamed Scottie by the others in my class. They laughed at me and wanted to know where my kilt was. They imitated me behind my back and they asked stupid questions: 'do they have cars in Scotland then?' 'do you eat baked beans in Scotland?' It seemed great fun to bully and isolate the new Scottish boy. Certainly no one wanted to be friends with me for a long time. I was not very miserable but then I could not be happy either. My defence mechanism was in overdrive - I did not care. I did not need any of them.

Eventually I managed to befriend one boy - he lived fairly near to us and he had Australian relatives. I went round to his house one Saturday afternoon and his dad told me that John was out in the fields. I set out to find him and when I did, he showed me his skill with a boomerang. I remember it as being the most amazing thing. It returned to him every single time. It was not a toy, John told me proudly, it was a real one, from Australia. I was dying to have a go and when he eventually relented, I threw it just as hard as I could. The boomerang disappeared into a dense wood. We waited with baited breath for its return, but it never came back. The rest of the day was spent hunting in the woods for the precious boomerang. It must have got caught in the trees and we never found it. John was heartbroken, he kept crying and shouting at me and when we finally parted that afternoon, it was for good. He never even spoke to me again after that. I had managed in one go to lose the most precious thing he owned.

Dad managed to find mum a job at the gunpowder factory where he had been working for the past few months. Now they both had pushbikes and would cycle off together in the mornings. The gunpowder factory made distress flares for shipping and routinely they would be tested. Flares would explode high in the sky far in the distance - fascinating at first but after a while we hardly noticed them.

Jack and I collected our water in a big red bucket from a tap at the far end of the caravan park and we would struggle back, water slopping out in a long wet trail. Eggs and milk were collected from Ash Farm down the lane and a goose egg from the farm opposite could feed all four of us! We ate duck's eggs, even a swan's egg once (totally illegally) - in fact anything that laid an egg was in danger of losing it to our frying pan!

The farm had large quantities of battery hens which lived in sheds situated close to the lane. It was quite eerie walking past the farm for classical music was played to the hens day and night in what seemed an extraordinary attempt to make them produce loads of eggs. But they almost seemed to cluck along as they laid in time to the music!

Outside the farm there was often a young man - much older than us, perhaps seventeen or eighteen who owned a beautiful gleaming motor bike. We would stand and watch him as he religiously cleaned it until it shone brighter than anything we had ever seen - it was his pride and joy. He was always aware that we watched him from across the road and every now and then would glance round to see if we were still there. When he was killed in a tragic road accident there was a terrible sadness throughout the village and Jack and I were profoundly affected by the emptiness that was outside the farm now. It was our first real encounter with the enormity of death and it frightened us.

Dad bought us bikes too - only old second hand bicycles, but they were great. I could not resist taking mine apart 'just to see how it worked', of course. Jack and I had a great time cycling around the village. For a short while I cycled to school but then the old Victorian school closed down and we all moved to the new village school about a mile further on. Now I had to travel by coach - the same coach Jack caught to his big school and the coach stop was by a fish farm where salmon were bred, and huge urns of milk were always awaiting collection by a lorry.

There was so much to see - it was country life at its best.....well almost its best - there was always home to bring us back to harsh reality.

****

Mum and dad were sinking deeper into their alcoholism and were drinking more and more at every available moment. They were very different drinkers really. Dad would now have been a quite quiet and reasonably harmless old drunk if he had been left alone, for he was definitely mellowing with age - he would have been happy with a park bench and a cardboard box, as long as a bottle was warming his hand. For as long as he received no aggravation from either his wife or her unruly sons, he was trying to relax into middle age. There was still a violent temper but it took a while to rile dad and Jack and I were nimble enough to keep out of his way much of the time. There had been times when there had been vicious and unnecessary beatings from him, when perhaps we had received a punch that he would rather have dealt to mum. But the main problem, the real emerging problem for us all, we now realised, was mum. She became very aggressive after a few drinks and would launch into vicious attacks of dad and anyone else who tried to talk to her. We had to keep out of her way when she had had a few for she became evil to the core - but for Harry, usually drunk and spread out on an armchair, there was no escape. She nagged and bullied him, shouted, moaned, swore, abused him until he could take no more. In the end he would lose his temper - that short fuse from the early days would light and he just had to hit her. She would retaliate and in the end there would be the usual full blown fight - it was always the same.

Every night, long after we had gone to bed, we would hear them coming home from the pub, weaving their way between the caravans, holding on to each other for support but arguing the whole time. They would stagger about in the dark looking for the right door, one of them would fall against the side and the whole caravan would shake as they tumbled into the darkness. The fighting and arguing continued until they both passed out for the night. Jack and I were so used to it - it was all normal for us. The other residents probably thought very differently.

I joined the Cub Scouts. Someone at work gave mum a uniform for me and suddenly I was a Cub! I dibbed and dobbed along with everyone else after school. I also grabbed boy's caps and tossed them up into the beams of the ceiling, I threw woggles up onto the roof outside, I broke the shield for Best Camper and I scratched my name on the bonnet of Akela's car. He asked me quite firmly after three weeks, not to come back. I was thrown out of the Cubs!

The run up to Guy Fawkes night 1965 was a time when dad was in his element. There was no need for us to buy fireworks, he said, he was making a brilliant firework for us at the gunpowder factory in his lunch breaks. This firework was going to be the most spectacular firework we had ever seen. We should invite all our mates round - if we dared - to see it go off, to see it light the sky in blazes of colour for miles around. This firework would be remembered for years to come. The build up was tremendous - Jack and I became quite excited. Only the faint memory of the helicopter incident held me back from inviting any friends round, so it was just the four of us who trudged down to a field on the drizzly night of November

5th, dad clutching a box with a fuse sticking out of the top, which was his firework.

We climbed over a gate and waited there while dad carried on walking into the middle of a field to light his firework. We saw the little flare of a match lighting in the darkness and dad attempted to light the fuse. He ran heavily all the way back to us and turned to watch. Nothing. The fuse had gone out. He cursed and trudged all the way back again, struck another match and lit the fuse again. He turned to run back to us but before he had managed four paces the firework exploded!

There was the most incredible bang and flash of light that lit the whole sky for a few seconds. It was enough light for us to see dad lying face down in the grass, then suddenly clumps of field were falling all around us from the sky. There were no pretty lights, nothing to watch. He had not made a firework - he had made a bomb! He struggled up and staggered back to us.

'Quick - run! Let's get home!'

I looked back at the field. There was a huge crater in the middle of it now. Our firework had blown a hole in the field and it was still smouldering! Jack and I laughed about it for ages but thank God no expectant pals had been there to see it.

A week before we broke up from school for Christmas our year had a special Carol Service at a church in Dorking. Everyone was involved. There was a substantial choir made up from members from both classes and everybody else played some sort of instrument. Considering I had had such a very musical father it was a great disappointment that I could neither sing nor play anything reasonably well. In fact I was a liability and eventually, just so as not to leave me out, the teacher reluctantly handed me a triangle and instructed me quite firmly that I was to 'ting' it once at the end of every verse, when she pointed to me.

Rehearsals went quite smoothly, and Mrs Hall obviously thought she had chosen just the right instrument for me - even I could not go wrong here. The Big Day came - a coach took us to Dorking and we all filed in, the whole church was full of parents, all chatting, but searching the children's faces to find that special one. My mum was there somewhere, I had told her all about it and I was sure she would be there, but I could not see her yet.

The service went well and the singing was beautiful, echoing round the church like an angelic choir, parents joined in when they should do and the whole thing went off suitably well. Except that I could not remember when I was meant to 'ting' now, and Mrs Hall did not seem to point to me anymore, so I 'tinged' along every now and then, whenever there was a quiet moment and I hoped that was the right thing to do. My triangle only made a little sound but I felt that because I was the only person with one, I must be very important and special and therefore I hoped everyone could hear it - especially my mum, wherever she was.

We all climbed back on to the coach afterwards and returned to school, some children had caught up with their parents for a brief word outside the church - I still had not seen mum but perhaps she had had to hurry back to work. Anyway, Mrs Hall was pleased with us all and we all felt happy that it had gone off well. At home later that afternoon, when mum arrived home from work, she did not mention the service and I asked her if she had enjoyed it. She said that she had. I asked her if she had heard my triangle and she said yes, it had echoed round for everyone to hear. I felt quite satisfied - that it had all been worth it just to please my mum.

There was just one tiny niggling thought that would not go away - that tiny thought that kept lurking around in the back of my mind - that perhaps she had not been there, she had not turned up. I do not know why I suspected it but I did. I always had this doubt when my parents were concerned and I did not know why. Or perhaps I did.

We spent Christmas in our caravan and it was pretty miserable, with no school to escape to and nowhere else to turn. They were both drinking a lot and Jack and I were alone much of the time. When they were at home with us they argued and fought and the caravan had become a dirty squalid slum.

Dad bought a car, a Hillman Minx, just like the one that had hit me in Penicuik, and now at night we would hear the car bringing them home. I suppose it muffled the shouting a bit. We had a head - on smash in that car down the lane. Although, luckily, no one was hurt, it really shook us up.

One afternoon during school holidays I found a pot of green paint and decided to paint some of the caravans. There was a huge confrontation with the Park Manager over it. I had a severe beating and we held on to our tenancy by the slenderest of margins. That caravan remained our home for quite some time.

Dad, as is so often the case with heavy drinkers, now had a problem with depression. It had been creeping on over the last couple of years along with his chronic alcoholism. Mum was often suicidal herself and managed to get tranquillisers 'for her nerves.' She was always threatening to overdose and end it all but she never carried it through and we all knew that. She used Jack and me as her emotional props, tried to make us tell her how much we needed her and would only finally relent when we collapsed crying, pleading with her not to send us to a children's home. Then she would seem to love us and care for us. But dad was different. His depression was deeper and he never feigned overdoses or threatened us with his impending death. He also had periods of total sobriety, something unknown to our mother, when he would alternate between talk of a depressingly hopeless future or great things ahead for us all. It was in the caravan that dad first tried suicide and he very nearly succeeded in wiping us all out.

I woke up in the middle of the night because I could smell something strange. It had come into my dream and was now forcing me to wake. I sat up and spoke to Jack but he was sound asleep. I got up and tried to shake him but he could not be woken. I felt my way through to where mum was sleeping alone in the double bed, but again, she could not be roused, and the strange smell was getting stronger. It was really horrid and I struggled to find my way through to the kitchen to try and find the source.

I could hardly believe my eyes. There, kneeling on the kitchen floor with his head resting on a cushion in the oven, was dad. The gas was full on and he was breathing it in as he slept. I lunged forwards and turned it off, then opened up the caravan door and stepped outside, burning my lungs with the cold fresh air. He was trying to kill himself - he could already be dead! He could have killed all of us!

After a few minutes I went back inside where the smell was definitely fainter. Jack and mum were still breathing. Eventually I roused her and together we heaved and hauled dad out of the oven and onto the floor. She took the oppportunity to kick his immobile body and curse at him. But he was not dead, I had saved him.

It affected me profoundly that he could have killed all of us. I had saved us all. That night I was a hero with no one to tell for nobody must ever know what happened at our home and we were pretty sure nobody ever did.

****

During the winter the caravan was heated with a paraffin heater. It was a bright orange unit with a detachable front which needed filling with paraffin regularly. It gave out good heat, enough for our little home and it could be quite cosy.

One evening mum and dad had been drinking and fighting as usual. A neighbour had even banged on the door and told them to shut up! Now dad was in a really bad mood and it occurred to me that he could be suicidal again. When Jack and I went to bed I opened the little window - just in case I needed an escape route!

We could not believe that he did it again. He tried to pour paraffin into the heater while it was still alight and of course, flames ran up the paraffin and into the can. Dad dropped it and flames were suddenly everywhere, licking up the sides of the caravan, engulfing the few things we had. Jack and I jumped up and ran through the flames to outside where we stood. It was freezing and we were in our thin pyjamas. Mum was sitting on the ground in the mud - she was drunk, she was angry, she was confused.

A kindly hand touched my shoulder. 'Come in with us,' said a voice. It was the lady from the caravan next door. She led us up the steps into their lovely clean home and sat us down. She produced two jumpers for us to wear and she sat with us on richly patterned floral seats. Jack and I looked around in amazement at the beautiful room - smart furniture, ornaments, flowery curtains. Tea was produced in posh tea cups, and cream biscuits! It was an experience I never forgot. Through the pretty curtains I could see the fire raging outside as our caravan burnt to the ground.

'We feel so sorry for you boys,' said the woman, and we looked blankly at her. 'But you mustn't worry too much,' she added. 'My parents used to fight a lot when I was little. It'll get better - you see.' But she did not understand, she really did not. There would be no change for us, it was always like this and always would be. Nothing, bar a miracle, would change anything.

Except that we had lost our home. We spent a night in that beautiful mobile home and most of the next day. We watched out of the window as various people wandered around surveying the burnt smouldering frame that was once our caravan. It was completely gutted. Nothing was saved, except the contents of our shed which included our bikes!

Staying in the caravan next door was another window into life outside of what we were used to. It was another glimpse at how other people, normal people, lived and both Jack and I longed for a slice of it too. For the first time it occurred to us that we might be happier if we did not live with our parents, but how could that actually happen? Who would want us anyway? The outside world looked at us as rough Scottish boys who were dressed in old tatty jumble sale clothes. I especially appeared hostile and mean, Jack felt the same but was more withdrawn. We were, without realising it at all, turning into the products of a deprived upbringing. It was probably too late to save us now anyway.

Chapter 6

Some time before mum had been offered a housekeeping job and she had pondered over whether to take it or not. Now a decision was forced on her and she made desperate phone calls in order to secure us with a roof over our heads, for this new job had a tied house. April 1966 saw us moving to a new home - an old Georgian cottage in Leith Hill, just a few miles away from the caravan site. Opposite us was Leith Hill Place where mum was to be housekeeper.

Our cottage was a semi-detached built in the very early 1800's, and it presented a perfectly symmetrical facade with a well worn brick path leading to the front door. In the centre of the first floor there was what appeared to be a bricked up window, but it was only ever a mock one with the lines of a window frame etched onto the cement in genuine Georgian style. Inside we stepped straight into the living room. A door on the left led into a huge kitchen with a sink and aga. In the corner of the kitchen, through an archway, was a spiral staircase which led to upstairs. Jack and I were up there in a flash, tearing through the house full of youthful excitement. There were three bedrooms and we bolted through each of them in turn. Everywhere was sparsely furnished and smelt musty but it was reasonably clean. Jack and I were thrilled - what a lovely house.

We clattered downstairs again. Dad had the side door open and had gone outside from the kitchen into the garden. We had a big shed and a good sized area of grass, overgrown, very neglected, but beyond the boundary, most interesting of all, was forest - like unexplored Amazonian jungle to us!

There was a small basic bathroom in the corner of the kitchen, obviously a more recent addition to the house - this was all luxury to us. It seemed an eternity and almost a dream since we had lived in a house with a real bathroom.

When we sat at the kitchen table that first evening Jack and I were both quite content. When we looked up at the ceilings we could see thick black beams - one of them looked like an old railway sleeper. We thought we could be happy here and we hoped this would be permanent.

It was decided that we should take the rest of the school year off and re-start school in the September and somehow we got away with it for no one ever checked where we were. We had four months to explore and play and run wild in the woods - the longest summer holidays ever!

A ginger cat came with our new house and he quickly became my pet. Because he was speckled with brown dad decided he was a tortoiseshell - the only male tortoiseshell in the world, he said, and I was thrilled that Ginger, such a special cat, had chosen to live with us. We did not have to feed him much for he caught plenty of mice and voles from the woods. He was a prolific mouse catcher and brought many home for us to view and deposited them on the kitchen floor. Mum was not at all keen. One day Ginger trapped a rat in the corner of the room - I never knew rats could scream so abominably. Ginger had his work cut out with this one but we stood and watched as he tackled it and killed it. The screaming stopped and Ginger, the huge hat rat dangling from his mouth, looked up at us then bolted out of the side door into the garden. Much later, full and contented, we could see him lying on the shed roof, basking in the sun, slowly licking the blood off his front paws.

Jack and I spent prolonged days in the woods while mum and dad were at work. We climbed trees, built camps and watched the wildlife. From up in the trees we spotted foxes and deer, saw rabbits hopping about below us and as evening fell we saw badgers emerge from their setts. We never went home until it was dark, and would collapse into bed, exhausted from all the fresh air.

When dad brought us home a little black puppy I had never been so happy. We called him Blackie and he was half labrador and half alsation, dad said. Actually he was the runt of the litter but we adored him. He never had to be put on a lead or taught anything - he ran wild with us in the woods of Leith Hill. I had two pets now, Ginger and Blackie. Ginger did not like Blackie quite the same as we did but he tolerated this stupid young pup from a distance.

Dad's new job was working nights in a factory in Dorking. It was ironic that he never seemed to have a problem in acquiring jobs, nor did he ever have difficulty in securing promotion. He always managed to hide his drinking, or control it sufficiently for a length of time to impress the bosses enough to become the foreman or the team leader. Then the drinking would take over and he would lose everything. He was no fool - he could have aspired to great things under different circumstances. I never saw him lift a paintbrush at home or tend a garden. Everything was sacrificed for the love of the bottle.

Now he needed transport to travel to his new job and he bought himself a Honda 50cc motor bike. Mum had lost her drinking partner for most evenings now, so she again took to hiding alcohol all around the house in various cupboards. Even the airing cupboard upstairs housed a couple of bottles. She would disappear upstairs every now and then and we would hear the cupboard door open very quietly, then the pop of a cork being pulled out, then the door closing again carefully. She thought she was totally safe in her secret. It never occurred to her that Jack and I were well aware of what was going on, she thought we did not notice as she slowly became more and more intoxicated throughout the day. If we ever mentioned anything she would fiercely deny that she had had a drink! She really thought we did not know anything. She was becoming a very sick woman.

Ginger the cat was killed in late summer. An ambulance went clanging down the road outside our house and Ginger, who lived his life at a speed much slower than anybody or anything else, just sat in the road and watched the noisy vehicle approach. He was just deciding that it may be wise to get up and get out of the way when the ambulance squashed him and Ginger was no more. Jack and I had to scrape him off the road and bury him in the woods. I was heartbroken.

To try and make up for the loss of Ginger dad took us into Dorking one Saturday and bought us two rabbits from a pet shop. They were speckled rabbits, six weeks old brother and sister. We brought them home on a bus in a cardboard box. As usual we had bought something with no thought at all - no planning as to where we were going to keep them and it suddenly occurred to dad that we would need a hutch. No problem, he decided - he would make one from the old bits of wood in the shed. He began banging and sawing in his attempt to make a rabbit hutch. To Jack and me the finished product looked all right but apparently our neighbour had provided the saw, nails, chicken wire and a catch. Dad proudly presented us with a hutch and Jeremy and Jemima had a home. Blackie the dog could not understand what they were or why they were in a cage. He thought they smelt incredibly tasty!

Leith Hill Place was, at the time, a private college for wealthy foreign students who came to England predominantly to study and to learn English. It was extremely grand and mum had her work cut out cleaning and polishing for hours every day. It took her less than two months to break into the drinks cabinet and she would return to the dining room regularly for a quick swig. It was the cleanest room in the place!

One of the students, who had come over for three months, was the nephew of the Sultan of Oman. He was about sixteen, a very handsome Arab boy with gold rings on his fingers and he was obviously a very eminent figure. He had two bodyguards, substantial men in suits, who had guns under their jackets and they followed him everywhere. We called the boy

'Sultan' because we could not pronounce his name easily and he was so friendly to us that he even invited us into the grounds of Leith Hill Place. We thought he was great. He spoke English reasonably well and thoroughly enjoyed playing with us in the woods - we showed him our camp. It was a little off-putting having the two bodyguards a few steps away from us all the time but Sultan would shout at them in a foreign language and they would turn away. He made them struggle through hedges, over streams, run after us through the trees - in fact Sultan made their job as difficult as possible. They never told him off - they accepted it all benignly and did whatever he said with total politeness. But they always had him in their sight. Only once did they call out to him angrily and that was when he was half way up a tree and he clambered down quickly.

It was a hot balmy summer's day when Jack and I met up with Sultan in the road and decided to go and buy ice creams each. Jack and I had no money but Sultan said: 'No matter - I buy,' and we all trotted along down to the corner shop. Once inside we looked into the freezer cabinet and chose our ice creams -'Fab's' - Sultan picked up five, one for each of his bodyguards too, who were standing outside, peering in. He put the five ice creams on the counter and the shop lady smiled, 'That'll be two and six, please.'

Sultan opened his wallet and from the back, from a huge wad of identical notes, he produced a crispy £20 note. Shop lady stared at it as Sultan offered it to her in his slender brown hand, then placed it on the counter. She looked at him in astonishment.

'I'm sorry, son, I can't change that,' she apologised. 'Have you got anything smaller?' Sultan pushed the note towards her again. 'No matter,' he said, still grinning broadly at her. 'Keep it all.'

I did not know who's mouth was open the most in shock - Jack's, mine or Shop Lady's. She slowly took it from the counter and stared at it, then looked up at us. 'Why thank you,' she emitted as we grabbed our ice creams and went. I glanced back at her as we walked away, and she was still examining her money. It was probably more than she took in a month. She could not believe her luck. I think she closed up shop for the rest of the week.

Sultan helped to fill our long days that summer and we really liked him. His stories were fascinating as we sat in our camp - how his family owned so many Rolls Royce's that if one ran out of petrol it would just be abandoned in the desert, how his dad had several wives and he had an assortment of brothers and sisters. When it was time for him to go it was really sad. He gave us his address and he promised he would write, and send us lovely presents. We missed him immensely but we never got any presents. We never heard from him again.

****

In September 1966 Jack and I were returned to school. Jack was twelve now and I was to be eleven in the October. Jack was gratified that he was returning to the same school - Archbishop Langton in Beare Green, a tiny village near Dorking, but I had to start another junior school and enrolled at Ockley. On the first morning we were dressed in our new school uniforms, reasonably smart, we thought, but second-hand of course. We were all discussing how strange it was that dad was not home. He usually got in from work before we even awoke, now it was eight o'clock and he still was not home. Mum lit another cigarette and wandered to the kitchen window which overlooked the front garden. We thought that she actually seemed quite concerned for dad as she paced backwards and forwards, glancing up the road and at the clock intermittently. They had a strange love-hate relationship, our mum and dad - we could never understand them.

Faintly, in the distance, we could hear his bike. It was popping a bit and did not sound quite right but it was definitely dad coming home. Jack and I went out into the front garden and dad appeared, a look of sheer pain on his face. He could not get off his bike - he pointed to his right foot and we went round to see what was wrong. His foot and shoe were bright red, glistening with blood. Blackie came bounding down the path, thrilled to see his Master. He threw himself at dad, all legs, tail and tongue and dad just smashed him round the head with his crash helmet. We knew he was in pain but that seemed really callous - poor Blackie never greeted him again after work. He never forgot what that crash helmet signified.

Dad managed to tell us that a car had collided with him at a junction. It had not stopped and because it was the middle of nowhere, dad had felt that the best thing to do was keep going and get home. For the first and only time mum needed to call an ambulance and dad was taken away to hospital. His sock was embedded into his foot and he was kept in for a few days. When he came out the first thing he did was sell his bike and buy a car - a Ford Zodiac.

My eleventh birthday passed practically unnoticed. Dad gave me a tennis racquet as I left for school - no ball, not even two racquets so I could play with Jack, just a racquet he had picked up from someone. In the afternoon I knocked clumps of mud on to the outside wall with it.

Shortly afterwards I was invited to a party! A girl in my class was having a birthday party and was inviting everyone in the class. I do not think she particularly wanted to invite me but it would have been too obvious to leave me out and anyway her mum just sent invitations out to the whole class. The girl, Alison, probably hoped I would not come, but I did - I had never been to a party before. We all stayed on after school and walked to her house in Ockley village. It was a palace - not far off the size of Leith Hill Place. All the children had carrier bags from which they produced party clothes to change in to and beautifully wrapped presents for Alison. I had no bag and no present. I took off my tie and undid my top button and hoped I looked sufficiently partyish. It was embarrassing not having a present for her though. We were all greeted by this perfectly groomed woman in a pretty floral dress, which she obviously had not slept in. She had dark curly hair and red lipstick glistened on her lips. She was a mother out of a story book.

Everyone quickly launched themselves into party games. They all seemed to know what to do but I just stood in the corner and watched. Alison's mother, perhaps sensing my awkwardness, asked me if I would like to help her lay the table and I followed her out and into the dining room. What a Table! Sandwiches, crisps, cakes, jellies, an enormous iced cake with 'ALISON' on it in big icing letters and eleven candles. I could not believe that all this was for us. Alison's mother kept disappearing in to the kitchen and reappearing with more plates laden with goodies. I was not much help really - I had no idea how to lay a table, but then I spotted a plate brimming over with beautiful fairy cakes, iced in white with juicy cherries in the middle. I could feel my mouth watering and I just had to try one!

With a deft movement that even surprised me I managed to snatch one off the plate, unpeel it from its little paper and ram it all in to my mouth. Every time Alison's mother left the room I chewed and swallowed and absorbed the delicious taste. Of course, one was not enough and before long I had eaten four cakes and was just beginning to fill my pockets with more (to take home to Jack, of course) when I was aware that I was being watched. Alison's grandmother had appeared from behind and stood spellbound watching me.

'What are you doing, you, boy!' she shrieked.

I turned. 'Shut up,' I said. 'Do you want everyone to hear?'

Alison's mother came back. 'What's going on?' she asked.

'This boy,' said the older woman. 'This boy - he's stealing the cakes - look at his pockets! Who is this urchin anyway?'

Alison's mother came over and quietly took her mother away. They stood in the kitchen talking, then the old woman came back with a little paper bag.

'Here you are, boy,' she hissed venomously. 'Put the cakes

in a bag at least.' She offered me the bag between her two extended fingers and I reluctantly took it from her. But I could not use it. I was beginning to feel really ashamed and embarrassed.

I sat at the party table with everyone else but ate little. I wanted to sing 'happy birthday to you' but words would not come. I hated it all and I wanted to go home. Roll on six o'clock.

Gradually, between six and six fifteen everyone was collected by their parents. All the children were taken away by smart caring parents who all seemed to know each other. At seven o'clock I was still waiting for my dad, at eight o'clock Alison went to bed and I was still waiting in the hall with a little brown dog for company. Alison's father came home from work and offered to drive me back to Leith Hill but her mother said no, to hang on for another half an hour, in case my dad had broken down and was on his way.

I suppose you could call it broken down, for when dad arrived at twenty to nine, he was extremely drunk, he had a bright red face and could hardly walk straight, let alone drive! I was so ashamed of him as he staggered into the hall way. I bundled him down the path and got him in to the car, Alison's parents watching from the doorway. They looked pretty concerned but dad was chuckling and happy and could not understand why I was so agitated. I do not know how he got us home in one piece but he did. I never went to a party again.

****

A very extraordinary thing happened to us in December. Blackie was about six or seven months old now and he was sitting in the living room with us one Friday night. We were watching television together and for once, they were both quite sober. It had been a really pleasant evening. Mum made a cup of tea about eleven o'clock and said we should go to bed afterwards.

Suddenly there were three loud thuds on the front door. That was odd because usually people used the door knocker, not that anyone ever visited us anyway. Eleven o'clock at night and we had a visitor!

Dad suspected it might be a tramp, for not long ago he had caught an old down-and-out in the shed, and he got up and opened the front door. Blackie started barking ferociously and dad, on seeing no one obviously there, sent him out into the darkness. There were no street lights, no moon, it was as black as black could be. Blackie vanished out into the night, still barking. Dad called out: 'Hullo! Who's there!' Suddenly Blackie yelped agonisingly as if he had been mortally wounded, then silence.

Dad called out for Blackie, but we heard nothing. Jack and I were both up now. Dad told us to get his torch and then bravely, he stepped out on to the front path. In the distance, from somewhere, we could hear a pathetic whimpering and dad followed the noise round to the shed where he found Blackie in the torchlight, a little bundle trembling in the corner. Blackie would not budge, so dad had to lift him up and carry him back in to the house where we were all waiting.

In the light indoors we all inspected him for injuries but there was not a scratch on him. As soon as we let him go he flew under the table in the corner and just lay there trembling all night - something had really scared him outside. Eventually we had to leave him there and we went to bed.

At seven o'clock in the morning there was a knock on the door - the knocker this time, loud and firm. Dad answered it and took in a telegram from a boy. It was from Scotland, to announce that his mother had died suddenly at eleven o'clock the night before. She had been a psychic in her younger days but had been in a mental asylum for years. Her 'gift' had driven her mad. We all looked at each other, we were all thinking the same thing - eleven o'clock, the knocks on the door, Blackie being absolutely terrified of something. Jack and I exchanged glances, we both felt the coldness pricking the backs of our necks. Had that been a message? We would never know, but dad never wanted to talk of that night again - it was a closed book to him. Whatever it had been he certainly believed in it and Blackie - well he definitely knew something had been there.

Christmas was always a good excuse for a mammoth drinking session and this one was no exception. It was permanently cold in our house but dad was able to swallow huge quantities of drink, then kneel on the floor with his head on a chair and sleep it all off in a drunken stupor. Mum had her supplies hidden everywhere and she managed to stay reasonably inebriated the whole time. Neither of them wanted to eat when they were so drunk and Jack and I crept around looking for food. Mum ran out of drink once, during a freezing winter's evening and she made me walk miles with her to the off-licence just so that she could buy a bottle of cheap sherry. She swigged at it all the way home 'just to warm me up' she kept repeating! Generally she tried to pretend she was totally sober and I often wondered if she ever guessed that it was Jack and me who went round all the cupboards and wardrobes to clear out the empties. She never mentioned it, but it was really frightening to see just how much she was getting through.

When dad awoke from his drunken sleeps, dirty and dishevelled, unshaven, with his hair, now speckled grey, all standing up on end, this was the time that mum would attack him. She had not shared a bed with him for many a year and sometimes to get away from her nagging he would shut himself away in his own bedroom. He irritated her beyond belief. We could not understand why she despised him so much or indeed, why he put up with it. But she was our real mum and our loyalty always tended to be with her.

This day, dad had disappeared upstairs to continue his coma and Jack and I were fascinated to see mum boiling a huge saucepan of water on the aga.

'What are you doing?' asked Jack.

'The bastard!' was all she would say. 'The fucking bastard!

I've really got him now!' The water was boiling, bubbling furiously on top, and with an evil glint in her blood shot eyes, she struggled upstairs carefully carrying the huge saucepan. Under her breath the whole time we could hear her cursing, 'The bastard...the bastard....'

Jack and I stood at the bottom of the stairs, listening. Dad let out the most almighty scream as she poured the boiling water all over the blankets as he lay in bed. There was a huge crash and thump as he jumped out of bed, suddenly very sober and then screams and more thuds as he beat mum to a pulp in the bedroom. When she eventually came downstairs her nose was caked in blood and her eyes were black and swollen.

'I'll get him yet,' was all she would say. 'I'll get that bastard one day.' She would never give up. Jack gingerly mentioned divorce being an easier option but she swung round on him and said: 'yes, but not as painful and I want to hurt the bastard first!' It seemed to us that she was getting hurt just as much, if not more than dad but she could never see it any other way. She was our mum and our allegiance was always with her so we almost backed her in her plans to murder Harry. Although Harry now had bright red skin he was not very badly burnt, it was like a case of severe sunburn. He emerged from his room a couple of days later as a mass of blisters! However, fortunately, the blankets had absorbed much of the heat. He had been very lucky.

Asleep in bed one night, I was suddenly awakened to see the silhouetted shape of dad in the doorway. He stormed across and grabbed me roughly by the hair and dragged me out of the bedroom, across the landing and down the stairs. I was screaming: 'Don't hurt me, please stop...' and he was yelling back at me in drunken fury. Downstairs he beat me and battered me until I was black and blue, he held me by the back of the head and smashed me against the wall, he punched me in the stomach and slapped my face and finished off by throwing me to the floor, kicking me and stamping on my arm. I struggled up again but acute pain made me stumble and I cried out in what seemed a thin tight voice: 'Please....please....stop....' He glared down at me, called me a snivelling little shit, turned and walked away. For a few minutes I lay on the floor somewhere between consciousness and unconsiousness, trying to make sense of what had happened. Then the tears started, slowly at first, and then in two rivulets down each cheek. I was sobbing and gasping for breath, so unhappy, so sore, so miserable that I wished I were dead. I was literally crying so much that I could hardly breathe. By the time I was able to drag myself back upstairs to bed every part of me hurt and I did not know what it was I was supposed to have done. But it must have been bad.

Jack found out what the reason was. Mum had put bleach in his beer and when he had tried to drink it and challenged her over it, she had said that it was Terry who had done it. I had had her beating and I never forgave her. Surely that was the upmost betrayal, the most unnatural thing she could ever have done. There was simply no maternal protection for her small sons. Twenty two years later when I broke my arm I found out that I had an old break in my left arm that had healed itself. I swear it was from that night.

I hurt for weeks - all down my left side was bruised black, blue and purple. I thought I was rotting. I was a mass of bruises and it even hurt to breathe. My left arm caused me much pain for considerably longer than the bruises took to fade. There was no way I could let anyone at school see my body so I never did PE again after that.

Dad, as depressed as he had ever been, seemed to think that rather than wait for someone to murder him he would rather get in first and again, one evening he tried suicide. He disappeared upstairs and nearly brought the ceiling down with a huge crash. We all ran upstairs to find him lying on his bedroom floor with a bit of string tied round his neck. The other part of the string was hanging from a beam in the middle of the ceiling. He had stood himself on a chair which he had kicked away as he tried to hang himself but the string could not take his weight. He only slightly sprained his ankle and was mortified that it had not worked. Mum shrieked at him in dismay too and told him there was much thicker string downstairs if he wanted another try!

The fighting was dreadful that winter - arguing and shouting incessantly. Jack and I would leave them to it and go to our camp in the woods. We made plans to run away from home and live in a wood somewhere for ever, but it was so bitterly cold.....still, anything must be better than getting caught in the line of fire.

In the spring when the first wild daffodils raised their yellow heads and the birds began to sing again, we were still in our winter of discontent. As usual, mum and dad went out every Saturday evening - in the car, they would not be long, they always said, they were just popping up the road. At about ten thirty in the evening we heard the car come back and dad came in alone.

'Where's mum?' I asked.

'Don't know and don't bloody care,' was his reply and he heaved himself upstairs with heavy steps. Jack and I sat up and waited. Hours later she burst in. She was wearing a big coat and she was totally dishevelled. Her hair was sticking up in some crazy style, her hands and knees were black with mud and she was covered from head to toe in bluebells.

Driving home from the pub they had been fighting and dad had leant across, opened the passenger door and pushed her out on to the road. Then he had driven off and left her there. Somehow she had managed to find her way home in the dark, sometimes staggering, sometimes crawling along the road but definitely somewhere along the way she had crawled through the bluebell woods! She was mad - a fiery mass of Scottish wrath. Harry was a dead man!

Next day we expected the worst but, amazingly, she was in quite a good mood - singing in the kitchen and doing housework, unusually occupied. She cooked a dinner, a Sunday lunch, of mincemeat and mashed potatoes. Jack and I were amazed that all was so normal. Why was not she having a go at dad for deserting her? He seemed to have forgotten all about it as well. There was just something in her eye that was not quite right. Every now and then she gave him the evil look and Jack and I still crept around uneasily. She was a vindictive, malicious woman and somehow we could not see dad getting away with anything. We all sat down in the living room with our dinners on our laps and ate. The silence was abruptly broken - dad cried out and spat mashed potato all over the carpet. Then he jumped up, his dinner tumbled to the floor and he rushed into the kitchen, spitting and shouting out in distress. He was in the kitchen for ages, we could hear the tap running and every now and again he would hurl abuse at mum through the doorway. She glanced at him almost in remote surprise and remained unusually silent. She had smashed up a milk bottle, crushed it into tiny fragments and placed the bits into his mash. She had wanted him to swallow it all, have his insides ripped apart and bleed to death! Again her plans had not worked. Harry lived to see another day.

****

In early June there was a School Trip. We were going to Hyde Park on a coach. Could everyone please pay £1. This was a trip for all the school leavers. I did not even tell my mum and dad about the trip. I knew there would be no £1 for me. She would rather I just had the day off school but to my surprise and delight I was not excluded and Miss Stephens took me aside and said that I was also able to go.

I sat quite happily on the coach that morning, travelling to London. Everyone was chatting and laughing and I tried my best to join in. The teacher walked up and down the aisle and gave instructions for when we arrived. We walked around the park all morning, we saw Marble Arch and walked down Park Lane with its beautiful grand houses. We finally sat down by the Serpentine for lunch and everybody started unpacking lunch boxes from their bags.

I carefully removed myself away from everyone and sat alone by the water. I did not want anyone to know that I did not have any food. It was yet again, embarrassing and awkward. Someone called out: 'Terry! Haven't you got any lunch?'

'Yes, I've had it,' I lied, dismissing it all as casually as I could. They turned away and forgot about me. I was always the odd-one-out, always different from everyone else.

Miss Stephens appeared at my side. 'No lunch, Terry?'

I could not lie to her - well not such a big lie! 'No Miss, I forgot it... but I'm all right - I'm not hungry.'

She held out a little packet in front of me, and an apple. 'I wonder if you could do me a favour, Terry,' she said. 'I brought far too much food and I'm going to have to leave all this. I don't want to waste it - could you help me out by eating it?'

I could not take it from her - she hesitated, then placed it on the grass in front of me, turned and walked away. I looked at it for a while, then turned and looked at everyone else - but no one was watching me. I grabbed the packet - none of it got wasted, I did eat it - I was starving.

A week or so after the School Trip, in a mad (and unusually sober) moment, dad bought me a go-kart in Dorking. It was a really nice one, hanging from the ceiling of the toy shop by wires. Before I knew it I was peddling down the High Street towards our car. Jack and I played with it for weeks. Peddling round the back garden one day we heard screaming from the kitchen. Dad was not around so mum must be screaming for a genuine reason. We rushed in the side door to see her chopping wildly at an adder with a wood cutting axe! She chopped and chopped and bits of adder shot out all over the floor. She finally stopped, wiped her brow and stood back to admire her handiwork. She was only five foot one, our mum, but that day she felt six feet tall! She felt she had saved us all!

In the summer holidays we had visitors. Dad's real sons,

Michael and Richard were coming to stay and he collected
them from Dorking Station at the beginning of July. We still
had two weeks of school and for me it was my last few days
at Ockley. I was leaving junior school and would join Jack at
Archbishop Langton in September.

Michael was my age but was much taller and stockier,
Richard was nine years older - twenty now and he talked of
his girlfriend back home and plans to get married. They were
nice lads and had had a comfortable life with their aunt. It
was quite an eye-opener to see their dad after such a long
time - for us it was the first time we had ever met our step-
brothers.

At first mum and dad were on their best behaviour. Michael
adored the rabbits and immediately dad produced another baby
rabbit for him. The new rabbit, Sooty, was pitch black and he
came with his own hutch. Michael said he was going to take
Sooty back to Scotland with him when he returned home.

We still had to go to school and we left Michael and Richard
alone in the house during the day. One lunchtime I was in the
playground when to my horror I saw our car coming up the
school driveway. Dad did not stop at the end of the driveway
- he carried on up onto the grass and bumped down the verge
again on to the playground. Then slowly he began to weave
around, in and out of all the groups of children who shrieked
and ran out of the way! Everybody stopped what they were
doing and stared at this mad man driving his car round the
school playground!

I rushed over and stood in front of the car, my arms
outstretched, then hands on the bonnet, in a desperate attempt
to stop him. He slammed on the brakes.

'Terry!' said dad, leaning out of the window. 'I've come to
see your teachers, son!'

Utter embarrassment overwhelmed me. I wanted to die -
how could he do this to me? He was extremely drunk and
very amiable, red faced, grinning round at everyone. All the
boys in my class began gathering around the car. Dad opened

the door and started to get out.

'Are you going now?' I said, urgency in my voice.

'Terry, son, are these all your wee pals?'

'Yes,' I answered. 'Are you going now?'

'Which one is your best pal, Terry? Do you want a wee ride in the motor, boys?' He steadied himself against the car.

'No they don't,' I snapped. 'Now, please...go...' desperate for him to go, please, please, just go...

It was one of the most humiliating times of my life but luckily he slowly lifted his heavy legs back into the car and drove deliberately away, weaving dangerously around the playground, away out the gates and down the road. It had taken me months to try and be accepted by everyone in my class. I really felt dad had blown it for me. Everyone gathered round me. 'What was he saying?' 'Was that your dad, Terry?' 'Does he always talk like that?' 'What was he doing?' 'Was he drunk?'

'No, he wasn't drunk,' I cried. 'He's Scottish - he always talks like that!'

It was the single worst moment at that school. If one of mum's murder plans had worked that night I would have danced for joy. How could he have done that to me?

Richard went home after a couple of weeks but Michael stayed on for a while longer. Mum barely tolerated him - probably because he was Harry's son, his flesh and blood. She spent a lot of time either totally ignoring Michael or blaming him for everything and nagging him continuously. The poor boy could do nothing right.

Every now and then dad would cook a meal. His famous vegetable (laced with barley) soup still made an appearance occasionally but generally he was into frying now and his huge frying pan would often produce meals for us all. One Sunday late in August when money was tight, he managed to dish up a real treat. Michael especially, was well impressed - we all were - there were even roast potatoes. Even mum said a few kind words to dad about the tender meat and delicious gravy.

Much later we noticed Sooty was not in his cage anymore.

Michael cried and dad insisted he must have escaped. But Jack and I guessed we knew what had really happened. We had eaten Sooty for lunch - he had only ever been destined for our stomachs!

Jeremy and Jemima were never intended for our dinner plates. Even so, they met a grisly end too. One morning we went out with carrots for them and noticed they were lying quite still in their hutch, even thought the door was slightly open. We opened the door further and peeped in for a closer look. To our horror we saw that they were both minus their heads! I screamed out in terror - two headless bodies lay together in a macabre embrace. Dad said a fox had had them but never in my life had I seen such clean wounds though - the heads had been severed as if with an axe . That fox must have had razor sharp teeth. Jeremy and Jemima were buried close to Ginger in the woods and we made little crosses for all three of them out of lolly sticks and twigs. We had lived through so much horror and death in our short lives but the demise of Jeremy and Jemima haunted me for a long time. I just hoped the fox with the razor sharp teeth never came back for me.

Mum was unbearably unkind to Michael. We were really ashamed of her at times. She spent days victimising him to such an extent that it was painful for us to watch. She picked on him all the time, wound him up, shouted at him, teased him sarcastically and was generally as unpleasant as possible. She probably felt that she was getting at dad through his son. She was now drinking heavily again. She would never have been so unkind if she had been sober and Michael just could not take it. One day he cracked up and screamed back at her through sprouting tears. We heard him saying that when he went back to Scotland Terry and Jack could come with him but she was a horrid lady and she could not come! He was only eleven years old but he meant every word of it. The sad thing was that she laughed at him and he ran upstairs sobbing.

Michael packed his bags and left soon after and Jack and I were left behind to pick up the pieces. Dad was furious at what Michael had told him and the arguing became more intense than ever.

Chapter 7

In September I joined Jack at the Archbishop Langton School in Beare Green. It was good to travel with him on the coach but I noticed a subtle change in our relationship. He had made his own friends in the two years he had been there and he purposely ignored me at playtime. I was forced to make friends within my year group so I hung around with a few boys I knew from Ockley School. It was a huge school in comparison to what I was used to and the headmaster was a tall thin nicotine smelling ginger haired man. I thought I would never find my way round or get to know all the teacher's names, but it never mattered for I was only there for three weeks.

For quite a while dad had been gardening at Leith Hill Place while mum held on to her housekeeper position by the skin of her teeth. They had caught her once at the drinks cabinet and she had had a warning. It was only a matter of time before an angry mistress confronted her with empty bottles. Mum vehemently denied touching anything but she was still sacked. She lost her job and we lost our home. We had to get out almost immediately.

Dad found us a new house at Norwood Hill, some twelve miles away. It was a brick built bungalow and was again, tied to a big house down a long farm track in the middle of miles of fields. Again mum was to be housekeeper. On the day we moved mum and dad packed all our clothes and belongings into the back of the car. Dad told us we could not bring our bikes - they would not fit into the car. But Jack and I could not just leave them behind. They were our pride and joy and we had had them for years. So we rode our bikes all the way to the village of Norwood Hill with sketchy directions to guide us. We were exhausted when we arrived at our bungalow. My bike limped home. The cotter pin had worked loose and needed tightening, but dad, in his wisdom, decided it was beyond repair and dumped it the next day - I was mortified!

It was the first time we had ever lived in a bungalow. We had a living room, a kitchen and down a corridor were two bedrooms. It was sparsely furnished but our few belongings soon made it home. Jack and I quickly moved our things into a bedroom and Blackie the dog chased around barking madly at all the new sights and smells. Next door to us was a farm.

We could not go to Archbishop Langton anymore. We had to start a new school yet again - my fourteenth, in Horley, a small town in southern Surrey. Again we had to travel there by coach. I was years behind educationally and despondent at school. I was in a low group for under-achievers with all the other 'undesirables' and struggled to concentrate on the easiest thing. To the school I was disruptive and a bad influence on the others - beyond any form of teaching and I needed a good caning at least once a week. I do not think anyone particularly disliked me - I was just treated with total indifference, but I hated everyone. I was sick of the effort of making new friends, sick of always being the new boy, so used to not understanding lessons that I spent my time thinking up new ways to be disruptive and make people laugh. It was the best way to conceal the deep insecurity - the best way to be liked - to act the clown and make the others laugh. Consequently I was sent out of many lessons and spent hours standing in corridors. All that achieved was to ensure I lagged even further behind as teaching continued the other side of the wall. I was the typical delinquent, behind the bike sheds for a smoke, walking out of school when I felt like it, sometimes not bothering to go in at all. There seemed absolutely no reason to go to school and there was certainly no parental backing or interest in what I did every day. Occasionally a teacher would spot me and shout out at me to stop as I wandered down the front driveway, but I would pretend I had not heard and just keep on going. No one really seriously challenged me about it all and I would never have given a civil answer to them if they had.

At home the drinking reached new heights. Now they were both absolutely paralytic all the time. Dad awoke from a haze one morning and, in an indignant moment, full of resentment and self pity, I told him quite truthfully that it was my birthday. He found a £1 note from deep in his back pocket and put it in my hand. 'Go on, now son, you go and spend this wee money, have yourself a good day....' he slurred, trying hard to focus on my hair so that he could ruffle it! But after school he demanded it back. He had run out of drink and needed the money. I had honestly mislaid it but he beat me black and blue in his fight to get it from me. Much later I found it on the front path and offered it back to him. He glared at me with an icy stare as he took it back. He thought he had won. His beating had worked.

So I was twelve years old now and I just wanted to grow up as quickly as possible. I felt as if I were an old man in a child's body. I had lived so hard, so fast, I was exhausted with it all. Jack was definitely affected by our impoverished upbringing too but he was very quiet and withdrawn. He had no real fight in him at all, the original pacifist! Our roles began to subtly change and I began to take on the role of the stronger brother and almost felt I had to protect him. I'm sure he never saw it like that. He was pulling away from me fast, making new friends two years above me. He could see the end of school in sight for him and he wanted to make plans for what he was going to do when he left. Jack was thinking about when he joined the world of adults and I was immensely irritated that I would be left way behind.

We did not even notice Christmas that year in our house. The whole world seemed to close down and turn into a decorated, colourful grotto, Christmas carols rang out wherever we turned - except at home. Our house was always freezing and cheerless. The alcohol seemed to keep mum and dad warm and they spent their days lounging around either in the living room, propped up on the old armchairs that had black, shiny arms, or sleeping in the bedroom on unkempt and unwashed sheets. Jack and I had to look after ourselves now. We had to earn money for food, for we were spending all our days starving, living on jam sandwiches and stale cheese. When dad passed out into a drunken sleep we would gingerly go down his pockets looking for money but there was never enough.

It was a bitterly cold icy winter that seemed to go on forever. Thick snow carpeted everywhere for weeks. An unearthly silent whiteness bloomed on the tree branches and hedges. The one word that describes our whole time at *Chantilly*, our bungalow, was 'cold'. It ended up being the worst time of our lives. Long pointed icicles, sharp as knives, hung from our front porch, glistening ferociously at dawn and dusk. Nothing seemed to move and grey birds flew starkly in the yellow skies. Trees cracked with the cold and every night the moon appeared, almost omniscient in the bleakness. After the school holidays we did not return to school. We were dirty, scruffy, unkempt boys and there was no one to make sure we did anything.

I cannot remember where they came from, but we seemed to acquire two air rifles. At the end of our small garden there was the huge hay barn which many rats occupied, scurrying around - huge black and brown rats, just as big as their Scottish relatives, if not bigger! Jack and I began to shoot at them from a position in the garden. Just very occasionally we would hit one and Blackie received a meal that day! We made spears too, shaping bits of slate into pointed arrow ends and tying them tightly onto sticks. We wandered across the fields looking for rabbits to kill - to cook for our dinner - but we never killed one!

One wretched January morning we sat on the fence outside the farm, huddled in our thin jumpers and tatty anoraks, frozen by the deathly cold. I had my collar pulled up as far as it would go trying to keep my bright red ears from dropping off with frostbite, shielding them from the bitter wind. Jack's hands were plunged deep into his pockets but I was gently stroking a donkey's face with one cold little hand. The world seemed to be an arctic prison from which there was no escape. A woman with weathered glowing cheeks came plodding over to us in her bright green wellingtons and thick snow coat. 'Do you like Dobbin?' she asked.

We nodded and she offered us a job. Would we like to earn two shillings each and clean out his stable and feed him? We started work immediately, totally exploited by yet another adult, and although this was better than just sitting about, we were so very cold. Purely to warm our red chapped hands we asked her if she would like her car washed and she produced a bucket of hot soapy water. We both immersed our hands in it and crouched there absorbing the heat. Our whole bodies seemed to be tingling.

We decided that this was the best way to keep warm so we wandered around for days looking for remote houses and cottages, offering to wash people's cars. It was worth it just for the pleasure we got when we put our hands in the hot water! Why nobody noticed these two neglected unkempt boys I never knew. No one asked us why we were not at school - perhaps no one cared.

Eventually we would have to return to our miserable home. Sometimes it felt like an interminable challenge - what would we face next? As we opened the front door the stale smell of cigarettes and alcohol would hit us like a wall and we would disappear into the freezing dark and get into our damp beds as quickly as possible.

Dad gradually sobered up enough to sell his Ford Zodiac and bought himself a little Honda 90cc motorbike. It could not have been through choice for we remembered him saying he would never get on a bike again - not after the foot incident. It must have been because he needed the money. One afternoon he staggered out to show us his new bike and give us a lesson on how to ride it. Jack and I stood and watched. The little bike had a flat battery and dad decided to bump start it. He had to run along with the bike and jump on to it when it fired. As the bike burst into life, he had the throttle full open but before he could jump on to it he fell. Instead of releasing the bike he held on tight and it dragged him twenty yards or so, on his stomach, down the gravel lane. Finally he had to let go and with a puff of smoke the bike fell on to its side and was silent.

We just stared at dad, lying in a crumpled heap, face down on the ground. Was he dead? We started to walk towards him and he moved! He struggled up, moaning a little. He was very much alive and as he turned towards us we saw the look on his face spelt fury! His jacket hung wide open, his shirt was all ripped apart at the front and was smeared with black mud and gravel. We did not wait for him to put the blame on us (for it was naturally going to be our fault!). We ran from him as fast as we could and stayed away for the rest of the day. There was no way we were going to take another beating. But the humiliation he had received had been complete! Yes, we were quite satisfied.

****

The farmer was an elderly man who had farmed the land there for years. He hired several young lads as his labourers and the work was hard and the hours long. We saw him occasionally as he drove tractors up the lane. He had a border collie dog called Badger that never left his side. But the thing we noticed most about him was that he always had a raindrop hanging from the end of his nose.

In February Farmer Drippy Nose spoke to us from the seat of his tractor. Would we like to join the lads who worked for him? It was still icy cold but the hard work did help to keep us warmer, it stopped us from freezing to death! We agreed to labour for him for a couple of shillings here and there. It never occurred to either of us that we were being exploited -

no one asked any questions and we did not have to tell any lies. But life was such hard work now and we were always hungry. Sometimes we took Blackie out with us and one day we lifted a corrugated sheet left out in a field, to see what was underneath. Scores of mice all darted out and Blackie, a dog possessed, snapped them all up as quickly as he could. It was the best meal he had had in ages. It occurred to us then that Blackie must be half starved too.

We loaded hay bales up high in the barns, we shovelled manure on to the backs of trucks. We sluiced out stables and helped feed the animals. We were real farm labourers now and the few shillings Drippy Nose gave us meant we could eat.

One icy morning Jack and I set off for the farm to see what joys there were in store for us. There was slight activity far over in the other side of the field and we could see Drippy Nose and his tractor and trailer. One of the farm lads, Emanuel, was trudging over towards the activity with a huge roll of rope. Jack and I hurried over to see what was going on. There, lying in the thick white snow, which was trodden down into slushy mud all around it, was a huge dead cow. Emanuel and John, the two labourers, were now tying rope around its legs and Jack and I stood and watched as they managed to haul the beast onto the trailer. We became aware of a man standing fairly close to us, also watching the little drama up on the field. He grinned at us and commented that farm work was tiresome, souless work in the long winter months. 'And they think I'm mad,' he chuckled. 'But I don't have to clear out horse shit and cow muck. I never get my hands dirty. They think I'm mad, yet I live in comfort with three good meals a day and everything done for me. Funny old world, isn't it?' And he strolled past us and walked slowly away, back to the mental hospital where he lived. He was a man whose words I never forgot. The old dead cow was taken back to the farmyard and later on that day they burnt it.

In March Jack had had enough and he started going back

to school. At least there was heating in school, he explained. I stayed on at the farm for a few more weeks. We had been lucky throughout our young lives that we had never really been ill or needed a doctor, but now I had a huge sore on my face that just would not go away. It started as a spot which I picked, then from under the scab it began to weep. Finally I had a huge weeping sore on my cheek and mum was forced to sober up enough to take me to see a doctor.

The two of us travelled into town on the bus. I felt like a freak - everyone was looking at me, I was sure. I fidgeted uncomfortably in the waiting room until it was our turn to go in. I had impetigo, a common organism, I heard the doctor say. I needed antibiotics and a cream to put on it and I must not go to school for a week. On the way home mum suddenly became aware of the fact that I had not been to school since December and she was adamant that I return in a week's time, once my impetigo had cleared up. It was ironic really - as if she really cared!

I re-started school after Easter. One or two boys were actually pleased to see me and I found I had a couple of mates. In a way it was almost a relief to be back really. It was a return to normal life.

The school was an early 1960's building - three stories high with a gym to be proud of. There were no real high flyers here but it was a reasonably successful school. The top two sets took 'O' levels (they were the squares - I never spoke to any of them.) The third set and a small minority of the fourth were in line for a sprinkling of CSE's (Jack was in the third stream), I was in the fifth, the absolute no-hopers, the kids with no brains, the delinquents and the fools. We were all the scrapings of Society's dustbins.

There was one boy in our year who was picked on more than any other, even more than me! His name was Edward Pennyfarthing and everyone called him Penny. It was pretty bad for him being lumbered with a girl's name but he was also small and plump. He must have come from a reasonably nice home for he always turned up at school in the full uniform with sparkling shoes and combed hair. He was in the third set but he had no friends there, so he tended to hang about on his own at lunch breaks. His biggest problem was really lack of confidence. There were several bullies in my class, real rough boys who stole from the small first year boys in a big way. Soon after I made my re-appearance at school they tried to bully me, but from nowhere I found a magnificent punch and sent one of them reeling - they never touched me again.

Edward Pennyfarthing was the odd one and I befriended him quite quickly. He helped me with some of the work and was quite a harmless little lad. He was concerned about being so small and fat but he was really pleased to have a mate. The 'stretching of Penny' started one Spring day and continued for weeks. The bullies decided that Penny was letting the side down - he was too small for the year and far too fat. Penny required stretching!

Every lunchtime they searched for him, they hounded him down like a terrified fox during the hunt. He was dragged, screaming his shrill little scream, into the gym which was full of boys from our year, and the doors were locked and bolted. One bully stood on look-out and three others carried him over to the horse. He was laid across the top of it and then the bullies measured him and started taking their money: it was sixpence to stretch Penny, tuppence to watch. For some macabre reason there was no shortage of volunteers - boys fought for good positions and waved their money in the air. When there were about six stretchers surrounding him they all started pulling. His legs and arms were outstretched, his smart uniform was flapping, Penny was screaming his high little squeak, 'Oh please stop - please stop - you're hurting me! Ow...ow... please stop!'

Boys were cheering, laughing, thoroughly enjoying themselves. The stretching of Penny went on and on. I always stood outside the gym, I felt powerless to do or say anything. Penny would have to fight his own battles. But he was weak and totally unable to stand up for himself. After he had been stretched he would be measured and they would all cheer to hear Penny had grown by half an inch or quarter of an inch or whatever it was

It happened at least twice a week and Penny became a boy obsessed with hiding from them all. I thought he was coping with it quite well, considering, but one lunchtime after the stretching, when everyone had left, Penny was still lying on the horse and I opened the gym doors and went over to him.

'Come on, Penny,' I said. 'Let's go and have something to eat.' He did not move. I went over to him and reluctantly touched his arm. Slowly he turned to face me and I saw the tortured look on his face.

Very quietly he said, 'I wish they'd just leave me alone,' and in the corner of one eye I saw a little tear.

Penny did not come to school after that. The headmaster announced in assembly one morning that Edward Pennyfarthing had met with a near fatal accident and would not be returning to the school anymore. We were all to remember him in our prayers and wish him well in whatever he did in the future. The rumours swept round the school like forest fire. Penny had tried to kill himself, Penny had been found hanging from a tree in his garden, Penny was lucky to be alive. The bullies showed no remorse. They chuckled about it, but I felt very responsible in a strange sort of way. I wished there had been something I could have done to ease his suffering. But at the end of the day we all have to suffer in life, Penny; that's what life is.

****

The latest lull in the drinking at home had finished and they both threw themselves into an alcoholic orgy once again. Mum would down gin, sherry, vodka - anything she could lay her hands on. Dad would polish off a couple of bottles of whisky and keep himself topped up with vodka and wine. If they both awoke at the same time and were aware of where they were and who they were they would erupt into violent arguments.

Sitting in school one day the secretary appeared with a piece of paper. The teacher took it, peered at it through her glasses and then looked round the class seeking out the correct pupil.

'Terry Steer,' she said. 'You are not to go home after school today. You are to go to Mrs Oliver's; apparently there's been an accident.'

My head was exploding, full of the most excessive ideas. What had happened? I could not wait to find Jack at lunchtime and he was looking for me - he too had had the message. If we could have we would have left there and then but we had to wait three agonising hours for the coach to take us home.

Home: cold, deserted, empty, blood on the front doorstep. We walked up to Mrs Oliver's, the owner of Dobbin, wife of Drippy Nose. She took us into her lovely clean warm house and sat us down. Gently, (so gently that we thought they must both be dead) she explained that mum and dad had had a fight. He had hit her over the head with a poker and she was in hospital - the police had taken him away. We were not surprised, we were used to it all. So they were not dead, it was not all over. When would they be home? Probably tomorrow, she said, as she prepared our tea.

Mum did come home the next day, a huge bandage round her head. Dad made an appearance in the magistrates court and was not released on bail, so aggressive and violent was he. Mum gave evidence against him and the final result some time later, was dad serving six weeks in Brixton gaol. One day soon after we returned from school to find mum gone. She had left a message to say she had gone to visit our gran and would be back in a week. It never seemed to occur to her that she was being an inadequate mother, she just could not think any differently and her views were distorted through alcohol. We, for our part, never judged her or thought particularly badly of her at the time. She was our mum and we still loved her, no matter what she said or did. At least it was a few days of peace and quiet. We tidied up the living room and threw scores of empty bottles down a disused well nearby. There was a little money in a drawer and we walked miles to buy fish and chips for three - for Jack, me and Blackie.

The worst thing about the whole incident was that it was all in the local press. I was asked so many times: 'Was that your mum and dad in the paper?' and of course, I fiercely denied it. No one must ever know it was.

Dad appeared back from prison with bags and bags of goodies. He was sober, plumper and happy. It was like Christmas - food filled our bare cupboards! But more importantly, bottles of drink filled our cupboards and within days, they were both in drunken stupors again.

Jack and I were worried. Mum's head still had not healed properly and one day she fell over and the wound split open again. She did not seem to notice the state she was in but Jack and I became increasingly concerned that she would die. The living room was a complete pig sty, bottles everywhere again, cigarette ends overflowing from ashtrays on the table, remains of old meals spilled out on to the floor, spilt drink, stains, and dad had even wet himself. The pungent smell of urine, sweat, cigarettes and alcohol was as bad as it had ever been.

So many times dad had managed to sober himself up, totally unaided by anything or anyone else. We had grown so used to seeing him lying in bed for several days at a time, heaving about in agony, suffering from the most dreadful withdrawal symptoms known to man, moaning and groaning in terrible pain, and then suddenly, after a while, being up and about, as bright as a button, sober and hungry. Every time it occurred to both Jack and I that this could be the beginning of a new sober life, but invariably after a few weeks all the good times would be wiped out - all his tremendous effort would be for nothing and dad would be drunk yet again. It was during his times of sobriety that he bought us the battleship at Portobello Road market and the go-kart in Dorking. He and mum were personalities utterly changed by the demon in the bottle.

Mum never really stopped drinking at all - she just varied from quite merry to absolutely plastered! She would never have been a strong enough personality to withstand the withdrawal symptoms anyway.

Now, concerned for the state they were both in, I remembered the doctor we had seen in Horley some months before and Jack and I called the surgery from a call box. The doctor arrived a few hours later. If he was shocked by what he saw he never showed it and he spent some time in that squalid room trying to talk to them. Finally he emerged to say that they had both agreed to go to hospital to dry out. This was a momentous moment in Jack and my lives - to think that they had admitted there was a problem and required help! Although we felt we had betrayed them by asking for outside help, our spirits were lifted by the distant thought that they may never drink again! I think the doctor left us a phone number of a social worker who could possibly help us, but mum tore it up instantly and the only occasion we were ever offered any assistance was thrown away with the rest of the rubbish.

Dad was taken away the next day by a taxi. When he returned three weeks later he was a real sober man who was supposedly cured. Mum, who never stopped drinking all the time he was gone, (but who insisted she never touched a drop) found it was her turn now and she reluctantly went off to the hospital for her 'cure,' cursing anyone and everyone as they drove her away.

After a short time mum acquired herself a job in the hospital kitchens. The advantage of this was that she could bag up all the left-overs which she gave to dad when he visited her on his little bike! He would then proudly dish them all up for our tea. I was absolutely disgusted by it all and went straight back to the days of barley soup - always checking I had enough pockets on me and unloading food in the back garden. Luckily Blackie was not as fussy and he would follow me out there happily, tail wagging, to gorge every pocketful eagerly.

Even before mum came home we heard we had to move. Mum had been sacked from her cleaning job at the big house months before but because she had not replied to any of the solicitors letters the law had had to work its long slow way in the process of eviction. Now dad was sober he realised what was going on and he informed us that our mother had lost her job and lost us our home! She had only worked a total of seventeen days at the big house in the eight months we had lived there.

Once again we were a homeless family. We had to present ourselves at the Council Offices in late May 1968 and hope they took sufficient pity on us. A woman looked us all over and offered temporary accommodation. She said there was a slight possibility that we could be re-housed on a brand new council estate presently being built in Horley. I silently prayed that it would be Horley. I did not want to change schools yet again. In the meantime we moved into St Anne's in Redhill, Surrey.

St Anne's was well past its sell-by date! It was an old people's home, a huge grey Victorian building that had a part of it divided into flatlets for homeless families. We occupied a small area on the first floor - two bedrooms, a kitchen and living room and down the corridor was a large bathroom which we shared with a few other families. We were just a family, a gloriously sober family who appeared to have fallen on hard times. Mum managed to get a job locally, dad acquired a new car - a Borgward which was really quite an unusual German car. For the first time he began to take an interest in his wheels - he tinkered around with it and polished it till it shone.

Mum did normal family things, like shopping and taking clothes to the launderette! She hung bits and pieces up to dry on a line in the bathroom and she went off to work every day. Jack and I travelled to school in Horley, about six miles away, quite happily on the bus and tentatively began to enjoy life. It was nice to come home, for the first time in years. We were almost certain mum would be in the little kitchen cooking a meal. There was no fighting, no arguments. Jack and I never ceased to be amazed at what the stay in the hospital had done for them. We began to think they were cured.

No one would have known we were anything than an unlucky but ordinary family - we began to relax. Blackie could not come with us to St Anne's. He had to stay in kennels in Newdigate, not far from the old caravan site. Every Sunday we went to see him and took him for a run. The four of us would walk through the woods together. We just could not get used to the fact that we were a normal family! So like everybody else. We did not care if we stayed at St Anne's forever for we were very happy there. The heating was always on when the winter arrived so we were always warm and well fed. The words of the stranger on the farm rang in my ears.

I was a teenager now - thirteen years old, not so obviously Glasweigan anymore, but mean and antagonistic with far too much attitude, not afraid of lashing out at anyone who poked fun at me. School was an endurance test - when I bothered to turn up. I was smoking a lot now (behind the bike sheds of course) and looking ahead to when I could own a motor bike and earn money. Life had not been a bed of roses but I had survived this far. Now I was bigger and stronger I felt I could cope with anything.

Chapter 8

In November 1968 we were offered a new house in Horley, just where I wanted, about five minutes walk from my secondary school. It was a brand new house, on a council estate and it was really for us. Nothing depended on it - there was no chance of losing it, as long as the rent was paid. It had four bedrooms so Jack and I had one each. Blackie rejoined us and spent ages rushing round sniffing in the small back garden, digging holes, full of excitement, thrilled to be reunited with us. We also had a garage in a block out the back. A local charity provided us with carpets and some furniture.

Mum was really pleased with her new house. She wanted the world to see it. Every few weeks she usually rang our gran and had a chat with Angus. Now she wanted them to visit. Before we knew it she was announcing that they were on their way to see us. We had not had any contact with Angus for over three years. He had been a spoilt, plump little boy when we had last seen him. I had spoken to him on the phone once or twice over the years but now we were to see him properly - nine years old and a stranger.

Gran was surprised and pleased that mum had been sober for the past few months and she obviously decided that the time was right for her precious charge to meet his family again. We watched them walking up the road towards our house, our necks strained long behind the net curtains, barging each other for a better view point. (It never occurred to us to rush out the front and greet them!) We saw Angus, chubby, cosseted, sucking a lolly, shiny shoes, hair combed slickly back, his gran walking along next to him. He was not like us at all - was he really our brother?

Mum loved every minute of the week they were with us. She had all her family surrounding her now and she soaked every moment up like a sponge - I can hardly remember a time when she was more contented, when happiness radiated from her and her eyes twinkled. Jack and I took Angus out with us for walks. He had a big thick anorak and woolly gloves. He was a bit sullen, but probably homesick, we thought. He talked of his mates back home and of all the aunts and uncles who spoilt him rotten. Jack and I began to feel irritated. We began to feel jealous.

A week later, on the Sunday, gran and Angus left. There were loose plans of Angus coming to stay on his own in the summer holidays. Jack and I wondered if mum would try and persuade Angus to stay with us permanently for we certainly had the room for him now. But we did not think he would be very keen and to be honest we were not that bothered about him at all. He was so different, we just did not know him and we felt he was intruding into our own world of secrets and untold incidents, of unspoken truths and unending endurance.

Early on Monday morning there was a knock on our door. It was the police with grave news: our gran had collapsed whilst getting off the coach at Glasgow Coach Station. She had had a stroke and was fighting for her life in hospital. The little boy who had been with her had gone to his aunt's house. Mum packed her bags and was gone within hours. As she arrived at Glasgow our gran died. Mum stayed for the funeral and when she reappeared six days later, she had Angus with her. Well, this was it then - Angus had come to stay for good!

Angus: all the words that described him - plump, spoilt, innocent, naive, stupid... Jack and I were not interested in him at all. He was not one of us. But so began mum's crusade of trying to make Angus love her. She scolded us for our indifference. Angus had had a tough time, she said, Angus had lost his gran and his home. Angus needed our sympathy and support. Jack and I could not believe it! After all we had been through, all we had seen and struggled through, all the homes we had lost - did none of that matter? Why was it of such concern that Angus had had one setback when we had had a lifetime of them? We really did not like Angus much. But he became mum's little boy, her favourite, her angel. She moved a bed into her room so he could be with her all the time. Dad slept in the fourth room. Angus got all the affection that should have been ours and he did not even seem to want it. He ate too much, he wanted too much. He walked into our rooms and helped himself to the few things we had. He was nine years old and he was a nightmare. The more we ignored him the more mum loved him. Life was just not fair.

By the beginning of 1969 it all started again. Jack and I returned from school to see Angus sitting on the back doorstep with his arm round Blackie, tears streaming down his little face. We opened the back door and stepped into the kitchen - we knew that smell so well. It was drink and there, in the front room, drunk as a skunk, was mum. She was talking to an imaginary friend about Harry. He was a bastard and she wanted rid of him, she was saying. She was, unusually, holding a bottle of vodka between her knees.

Jack and I turned and walked out, our spirits as low as they had ever been. We had always known, deep down, that this would happen. The repetition was like a curse. We led Angus away and tried to persuade him that all would be all right again soon. Angus was a small vulnerable boy and he was terrified.

Very quickly dad started drinking again too and our lovely new house became the pig sty we were so used to. We could hear Angus crying for his granny at night and he desperately wanted to return to Scotland. There seemed absolutely no point in trying to make our home habitable. Dog hairs lay thick on the carpet and furniture, human hairs hung from the backs of chairs and various body fluids stained the seats. Uneaten and forgotten meals were strewn throughout. The cooker, rarely used but somehow filthy, seemed stuck to the floor with yellow grease. The overpowing smell was of dirt and neglect, dampness and drink. As we lay in bed at night we would hear the incessant arguing downstairs - intermingled with the occasional crash and thud.

As usual mum wanted Harry out. She hated him, she loathed him, he was the root of all evil. She locked the doors after him when he went out one day and packed a suitcase which she left on the doorstep. Dad was not to be beaten so easily. He stood outside the back door when he returned from the pub and shouted obscenities for a few minutes. When she did not let him in he simply smashed the glass door with his bare fist and crawled in through the hole he had made. Mum and we three boys charged out the front and waited until he had fallen asleep. Then we crept back in and hoped he would have forgotten all about it by the time he awoke. He was not even cut - how could one person be so lucky? Our back door was now boarded up.

Mum managed to control her drinking to a certain extent and she started another new job, cleaning in a school. She made a friend, a fellow cleaner who also frequented the same pub, and lived quite close to us and this woman, Pat, became mum's confidante and drinking partner when dad was out.

News spread fast among our Scottish relatives that Alice had a nice big house and it was not long before two cousins arrived to visit - Trevor and Gordon. They were the sons of mum's older sister, aged twenty three and twenty one. They were the toughest men for miles around back home and they too came from a rough alcoholic family. Gordon had been in the army and had served in Northern Ireland against the IRA. He was full of stories about the armed forces and confessed that he had murdered several members of the IRA. Trevor had just been released from prison. He had served two years for burglary. If the truth were told Jack and I were very scared of them. They had come to stay for a fortnight, although dad was totally against it. He did not like either of them and it was the cause of fresh arguments. They shared my bedroom and I moved in with Jack.

Trevor was a thoroughbred criminal. There was not an

honest bone in his body. One evening I tried to get into my bedroom to get some clothes but I could not open the door properly. Something was blocking the way. 'What do you want?' Trevor said curtly.

They dragged something away from the door and let me squeeze in. The room was absolutely full of televisions, record players, tape recorders - masses of equipment, piled up high. My face must have shown pure shock.

'It's just stock,' said Trevor, by way of explanation.

'Where did you get it all?' I asked. They had burgled my school and some local houses. I could not wait to tell dad when he got in from work. (I wonder why - did I relish the thought of dad, Jack and me being on the same side, united in our hatred of Trevor and Gorden - did I think this was the best weapon to get rid of them? Or did I subconsciously note the way mum loved her Scottish relatives so much and yet neglected her own sons every day?) Dad stormed upstairs - he could be an intimidating man when he wanted - he was certainly no push-over now!

'Get that stuff out NOW!' he yelled. 'How dare you bring this into my house! I'm going out - when I get back it had better all be gone or you'll get it down your throats!'

Satisfaction... I sat in the living room listening.

Trevor and Gordon began to bring all their goodies downstairs and stacked them all out in the garage. Somehow they had to dispose of it all. Trevor poked his head round the door and looked at me angrily. 'You little grass,' he sneered, pointing. 'Back home I'd bloody punch your lights out!' My heart missed a beat. Oh God, what had I done?

Trevor must have sold his wares for he was flush with money a few days later. He was pill popping now and carting crates of drink up to my room. He and Gordon were having a holiday, drugged and drunk and having a ball!

When Spring came Trevor and Gordon had been with us for two months and I was relieved to see Gordon, at least, had gone when I returned from school one day. It was such a relief but I was still quite scared of Trevor and I hoped that this was an indication that he too would be on his way soon.

Dad was irate beyond belief that they had stayed so long. He had not forgotten the treatment mum had given Michael and now it was his turn to get at her through her nephews, not that it bothered Trevor in the slightest. Just in time to take Gordon's place, we heard a knock on the door one evening and who should be standing there but a fair young girl who announced that she was Trevor's wife! To say we were astonished was an understatement! She was Glynis, she said and Trevor and she had been married for three years! Trevor had never even mentioned her and he was furious when he saw her, sitting in the front room drinking tea with mum. He cast her sideways glances of pure hatred. She was such a pleasant person, we could not understand how she could have got married to Trevor. As if it were yet another incentive, mum began to behave herself and managed to stay reasonably sober most of the time Glynis was with us.

In June we had a Sports Day at school and as I liked the games teacher and he had personally asked me to attend, I decided to show. I was lining up for the 100m race when I saw my mum and Glynis arrive and stand with the other parents and spectators. It was the first and only time mum ever supported me in anything to do with school. Although she was not totally sober she was in a reasonable state and she and Glynis watched me win my heat. I think their presence inspired me for I won the final too.

The arrival of Glynis added fuel to dad's fire and he was even more angry that Glynis had settled into our home as well. There seemed to be no talk of them leaving. Mum quite enjoyed Glynis's company and she loved irritating dad! But dad wanted them out. Mum accused him of being petty and unreasonable and she wanted them to stay - they were family. She launched herself into her usual battles with dad and the more he wanted them out the more she wanted them to remain with us indefinitely. After one particularly nasty argument dad packed a bag and left. We heard his Morris Oxford car start up out the back and he was gone. Mum was thrilled - she had won the latest battle. She had got rid of him! 'Glynis,' she said 'You can stay as long as you like!'

Jack and I thought he would be back in the morning but he did not appear and we began to think he had really left us.

Trevor's drug taking was increasing and he was getting careless. Pills were being left about in the bedroom quite casually. One day mum found them all and was livid. I watched her as she angrily threw them all down the toilet, flushing it repeatedly as soon as the tank refilled, trembling with the excitement of what she was doing, elated by the rush of adrenaline. 'The bastard's not taking these - he'll bloody kill himself!' she said. (Surely, not a bad idea, I thought.) When Trevor came in from the pub he went up to the bedroom, saw his supplies had gone and went mad. We heard him shouting and swearing, hurling furniture about and cursing everyone. He stood at the top of the stairs and yelled down: 'Where's my stuff?' Mum shouted back: 'You're not taking them here. I've thrown them away.' (It was odd how moral she had suddenly become for her own bedroom was awash with pills!)

Trevor calmly walked into the bathroom and slit his arm from elbow to wrist with a razor blade, then ran downstairs and sat on a stool in the middle of the kitchen, ready to bleed to death. Blood spurted from his left arm which he was supporting underneath with his right hand. The flesh had actually opened up and blood poured from him and gushed all over the floor. Trevor just looked at us all panicking but showed no emotion, said nothing. Jack charged next door and phoned for an ambulance. Just as he was passing out, the ambulance men burst in, wrapped Trevor up and took him away. Mum, Jack and I spent hours cleaning up the kitchen, the stairs and the bathroom. There was literally blood everywhere - even up the units in the kitchen. Trevor's life was saved that night and when he came out of hospital he and Glynis moved back to Scotland.

****

We were nearing the end of the school year and Angus was not quite so distraught all the time now. He always had Jack and me to look after him and generally as soon as any aggression started he would disappear out the back door with Blackie. Now that dad was not around it was generally more peaceful anyway.

Considering how neglected we had been throughout our lives it was relatively surprising that we had not come into conflict with the long arm of the law. However, all that changed when a friend from school, Sam, and I discovered the Coal Yard!

The yard was in a quiet part of town and every evening after the lorry drivers had finished their deliveries they parked up the vehicles, locked the gates and went home. Lurking outside, watching quite by chance one evening was Sam and me. A little later we managed to hop over the fence and went to investigate.

The coal lorries were huge. I tried the door of one of them and to my amazement it opened. I suppose they were the days when vehicles could be left unlocked and the owner would almost be certain they would be untouched in the morning. I was the confounded nuisance who changed everything. I clambered up and sat in the cab. Sam tried the door of another lorry and that was not locked either. We sat in a lorry each and grinned. I glanced down at all the controls and levers. There, twinkling in front of my eyes, was a key, still in the ignition, almost still warm from the driver's hand! I turned it and the lorry shuddered into life. I did not know a lot about driving - only that you pushed the clutch down, heaved the gear lever about and pushed on the accelerator - but I was a quick learner, and within minutes I had driven my lorry a few feet, and managed to brake as well. Sam did the same. We were driving!

Enough was enough for our first drive. We scampered away, thrilled and excited. Night after night we returned at six o'clock to drive our lorries. As we manoeuvred them around the yard we scraped along walls and hit various things, but nothing too serious, no real damage. We became really bold now. We managed to unlock the gates and drive out on to the road. We drove around in the town - very slowly, being as careful as possible, but we were really driving and it was great fun!

On the eighth night we arrived at the yard as usual. All was in darkness. It was almost too quiet and I think I knew that something was wrong. As I climbed in to my lorry I thought I saw a movement behind a hedge some way away. I stared at it, but nothing. I must have been mistaken. Sam and I both started our engines and the lorries thundered into life. Suddenly my door was flung open and there stood the meanest burliest bunch of men I had ever seen. They grabbed me ('Get down here you little shit!') and dragged me down from the driver's seat and proceeded to give me the beating of a life time. Sam was receiving the same treatment a few feet away. We screamed and fought back wildly, legs and arms flailing, but it was no fair fight. We were both held by our hair with our arms pushed roughly up our backs and we were frog-marched all the way to the police station. During the walk I was kicked continually from behind by one of the men.

Mum had to be called and statements had to be taken. I was so bruised I could hardly sit. Mum was probably more annoyed that I had been beaten up so viciously than she was by my crime. I had to see the doctor the next day and he firmly advised taking legal action against the bullies. We were only thirteen, he said and nothing warranted this sort of beating. I never knew if the thugs were punished but it was probably highly unlikely. But that signalled the end of our trips to the coal yard and it also meant the end of Sam and my friendship. His parents banned him from seeing me any more - I was a very bad influence.

****

It was Saturday evening and we were watching television. when the back door opened and mum burst in, with her chum, Pat following close behind. Mum carefully removed the big mirror which hung on the wall above the fire. We looked up at her with puzzled faces.

'Pat knows about these things,' she said by way of explanation. 'Terry - get the table into the middle of the room.' She carefully placed the mirror onto the table. She had had quite a bit to drink but she was not too bad. With a bright red lipstick Pat began to write letters round the edge of the mirror.

'You're not doing a ouija board,' laughed Jack.

'We certainly are.'

'Mum, they don't work - they're all fixed.'

'No,' said Pat. 'They're very real. You see....'

Pat had finished writing all the letters and mum produced a glass. We all had to sit down with our fingers on the upturned glass which was in the centre of the mirror. Mum and Pat were so serious, Jack and I were curious but we were totally disbelieving. Pat put on her most sincere voice....'Is anybody there? Spirits - speak to me....'

Jack and I both grinned at each other. It was like something out of a film!

After a while mum and Pat began to push the glass. A name was spelt out: **KING FRIEND.**

'What the hell's that supposed to be?' laughed Jack.

Pat looked at him sharply, 'Kingfriend is my Spirit Guide,' she said. 'He nearly always comes through to me.'

Jack and I exchanged glances again - what a fix!

'Tell me, Kingfriend,' said Pat. 'Are we to get money? Is there good fortune on the horizon?'

N...O...the glass moved.

'Oh stop it,' I said. 'This is really stupid.'

'You're both pushing it,' accused Jack. Both Jack and I

removed our fingers from the glass and sat back in our chairs, I swung backwards and balanced on two legs. We both watched sceptically.

'Have you anything to tell us?' asked Pat, ignoring us and making the most of her avid audience - mum.

N....O...said the glass.

Mum interrupted - 'Ask about Harry! Go on - ask about him.' Her hand was trembling, a thin boney finger pressing the top of the glass.

'Where is Harry?' said Pat.

P....U....B....

'You're pushing it,' repeated Jack. 'I can see you are.'

Mum and Pat ignored us.

'He's up the pub,' said mum. 'The bastard - see, he's got money, Pat - what did I tell you? He's spending my fucking money. He's got my allowance book and he's cashing my money!'

The glass began to move - so fast mum's finger got left behind. Pat was pushing it on her own - she had to be. The glass spelt out H.....E....R....E...

'What?' exclaimed mum 'Who's here?'

'Is Harry here?' said Pat to the glass.

Y.....E....S......a little slower this time.

'Well, he's not here, is he,' said Jack, smugly. 'So that's wrong isn't it!'

Mum and Pat both took their fingers off the glass and suddenly, slowly, silently, is if it were hovering slightly above the mirror, the glass began to move alone.

It spelt out G....O....

'Go,' said Pat.   G......O....it repeated.

'What, us?' said mum alarmed. 'We should go?'

Jack and I both sat forward, our flesh crawling, suddenly interested. This was real!

G....O....N....O....W....the glass moved on its own. Then it shot to the very centre of the mirror and stopped. It never moved again.

I was really frightened now. There was a strange electric sensation in the room and nobody spoke. Why should we go? Was worse to come? Had that been a warning that we should get out quick? As the back door opened we all cried out, in pure fright. Two seconds later Harry walked into the room.

We never knew where he had been for the past three weeks, he never told us, but wherever it was he had decided it was better at home and he was back for good. Mum almost seemed pleased to see him - or perhaps she was just relieved it was not Kingfriend or any other unwelcome spirit!

Whatever else Harry was he was mum's faithful drinking companion and between them they kept the local pub in business. It was a real old dump of a pub. It even had sawdust on the floor and the seats were ripped and stained. There were no frills here. But then mum and dad did not need frills, they just needed alcohol - beyond food, home comforts or the well being of their children. Their drinking gradually increased over the next few weeks and it was left to Jack and me, yet again, to carry out the same old necessary chore of clearing out the empties on Saturday evening when they were both out. Mum hid her bottles in the most ingenious places. There was even half a bottle just inside the loft!

Once, at the end of our tether, fed up with watching mum drink herself into oblivion, we tried something different. We emptied all the drink we could find down the kitchen sink. We thought that maybe if she did not have it around the house she would sober up and all would be all right. We were angry with her for neglecting us and wanted to hurt her as much as possible. She was absolutely livid with us. Jack and I were both taller than her now but she grabbed a shoe and hit us both round the head and faces and shrieked abuse at us - we were the sons of devils! We should have been drowned at birth! How could she cope with her nerves now? Next day she simply went out and bought loads more.

Mum rarely went to an off-licence for her drink - nothing so obvious. She would potter about the local supermarket for ages, picking up little bits and pieces for her basket. Then, as if it were an afterthought, she would wander casually over to the drink section and ask for a bottle of sherry and gin. She put on a brilliantly casual act as she went through the checkout, though almost unable to conceal her addiction. Then she would charge home as quickly as possible to start her binge. All that shopping - all those useless things she came home with - all in the pretence of being normal, but just to get a drink.

Dad was quite different. He would march into an off-licence and buy an assortment and he did not care who knew it. He never ever came out without a bottle under his jacket which had not been paid for! Even when they were unemployed there was always the £13 per child per month from the Auchengeich Disaster Fund to keep them going.

****

We were sitting in school in November 1969: Geography - New Zealand. Very bored, soon time to go home......

'Terry! What's so interesting outside?'

'Nothing.'

'Then tell me what I just said.'

'What you just said?'

'Yes,' she stepped towards me. 'About the South Island.'

'The South Island? Well, it's an island, surrounded with water.'

I grinned. She stared at me. 'Terry - you just don't listen, do you?' she said, exasperated. 'Have you learnt anything this lesson?'

'The South Island's an island,' I said. Stifled laughter rippled round the class.

'If I thought you'd do it I'd set you extra homework, but you really are a complete waste of time. Have you ever thought ahead to what you are going to do when you leave school? Have you thought about who would want to employ you?

You're going to leave this school with absolutely nothing!'

I just grinned at her. Bravado... always worked.

The bell went. Instant action: everyone scraping chairs, gathering their books, talking and leaving. I moved forward to go, but the teacher leant forward and touched my arm: 'Terry, can you wait behind a moment?'

I stood still, wondering what punishment I would get for not knowing about the stupid South Island. The last pupil left the room and closed the door behind him.

'Sit down, Terry,' she said and pulled up a chair in front of me. I sat reluctantly, uncomfortable in her presence. She was young and pretty, she smelt of perfume and had a fluffy jumper on and a swinging necklace. She was sweet and kind and she cared. Deep down some raw sexual awakening was stirring inside me and I was suddenly very aware that she was a woman and I was fast becoming a young man. The sensation of being alone in her company was almost too embarrassing to bear.

'Terry - is there something wrong?' she asked. 'Is there something you'd like to talk about?' I looked down at the floor, said nothing.

She persevered. 'Why are you so unhappy in school? Why don't you want to learn anything? You're the same in every lesson, aren't you - all your teachers say so. They all think you are a waste of time and effort. But I think underneath it all there's a good boy - what's wrong?'

Still no response from me. I continued staring at the floor. Bet they all discussed me in the staff room - cocky little Terry Steer, rude and aggressive, nasty piece of work. If only they knew...

'Have you got problems at home?'

Slowly I looked up and for the first time met her gaze. Problems at home: interesting one, that!

'Please, Terry - tell me - I know someone who could help you, someone you could talk to. I know you're not all bad. Why do you play the fool? I know you've got a good brain up there' (she tapped my head!) 'Why don't you use it?'

I still met her gaze for a second or two, then looked down again. Problems at home. Well, where should I start? I was fourteen years old and no one had ever asked me before if I had a problem or if I would like help. No one had ever spoken to me like this before. Where would she like me to begin, I wondered. What should I tell her? What could I tell her about life at home? The drinking, the continuous suicide attempts, pill taking, drugs, fourteen schools, being bullied, being abused, gin, whisky, vodka, sherry, ouija boards, so many homes in so many places, houses set on fire, and the fighting....yes, the savage fighting... all the arguing, the blood, hospitals, so cold, so hungry... Jesus, is this my life? Am I thinking about me, and Jack and our life together? Does anyone else live such a life? This woman - this Miss Tidy, what would be the point of telling her anything? She would never believe me anyway...

'Terry? Is there something you'd like to tell me? It would go no further, I promise. Unless you'd like me to speak to my friend. I know he could help you, he sees lots of troubled children...'

'Nothing,' I said, interrupting her and fidgeting in the chair. 'There's nothing wrong. Everything's fine.'

She knew it was useless to try any more. I was sullen, restless, uncomfortable and she let me go. I thought about it walking home. She had given me a chance, had Miss Tidy. She was like a tiny light in the darkness that was my life. I liked her, she was kind and she cared, but I could not tell her anything. No one, no one must ever know about my home - never. It was a secret that we boys kept to ourselves; we had an unspoken pact of secrecy.

Chapter 9

At the age of fourteen and a half my relationship with my dad changed completely. He had always been a strong man, who lashed out belligerently after a few drinks, especially when mum was winding him up, as she did so effectively. He was very quick to punch us and he had often beaten us viciously. Jack and I were small thin boys for so long. It was incredibly easy for him to beat the daylight out of us to ease his frustration. Occasionally I, especially, needed a parental slap but I never deserved the thrashings I had regularly received.

Dad was having yet another go at me. I answered back and he glared at me with his red-rimmed drunken eyes. He was threatening me further - I answered back again. As he stood up to come over and slap me round the head I rose to meet him. I challenged him. I was bigger now, I was prepared to fight back, to give it a go, try and defend myself anyway. Surely I could run faster than him - he was only an old drunk! Dad saw me rise. I was slightly taller than him now and I could see him weighing up the situation. I stared at him almost in slow motion, with the most menacing face I could muster, I looked at his balding head and his straggly white hair, his red bloated face and his aged body. To my relief and amazement he slowly backed off and sat down again.

I sat down as well, deliberately slowly, still looking at him. The challenge had been assessed and he had decided he did not want to risk it. He never ever hit me again.

Walking home from school one afternoon I reached our garage block and as I turned to go down the alleyway to the back garden, I could hear shouting - mum's voice, shrieking, screaming, swearing - then dad's voice, low, very angry, shouting back at her with pent up frustration. A few steps nearer and I could hear her words: 'I'll fucking kill you, you bastard!' Then his enraged voice again, still unclear, bellowing back at her.

Young children were standing at the end of our garden, watching. I could not see what, for a brick shed was blocking my view, but a few more yards and I could observe the action too.

They were in the back garden, dad in a dirty white shirt with just one button in the middle done up, baggy trousers, grubby, stained. Mum was also in a shirt and trousers and she was clutching an ornamental sword that usually hung in our living room. Dad had hold of a huge bread knife and they were literally hacking chunks out of each other in what looked like a macabre sword fight. As mum kept putting her left arm up to protect her face, he kept hacking away at her arm and blood was everywhere. She was attacking him mainly on the top of the head, plunging the massive sword down on to him, slicing his scalp, and blood was pouring down the front of his shirt.

I ran at her from behind (for she was definitely the more dangerous) and grabbed her weapon. She was still screaming, at me now as well. Somehow, without being slashed at all, I managed to get her into the kitchen and disarmed her. Then I seized the knife off of dad who had sunk into a little exhausted heap in the garden. Pulling him inside too, I slammed the kitchen door to shut out all the spectators. Mum's arms were both bleeding and I tore up two tea towels to make bandages. She hurled abuse at dad the whole time. He stood at the kitchen sink, dabbing water onto his head, shouting back at her.

At some point Jack walked in on this scene and the situation gradually diffused. Later I found Angus hiding in the bathroom, ten years old now, and trapped as we had always been. I recognised the look in his eyes and I felt a surge of pity for him. But Angus always had Jack and me to lean on. We had

had no one.

Mum wanted Harry out more than ever now. Harry was the son of the devil, root of all evil. Most of her married life seemed to be full of hate for Harry and trying to get him evicted. In turn Harry now threatened her with eviction. He was going to throw her out and her three boys! She went to the Council Offices to get her facts straight and found out there was no way he could evict her, not with her sons. But unfortunately the tenancy was in his name only, so it was a shame, but she could not throw him out either.

So she was stuck, we were all stuck, destined to continue living together in this hell hole.

Probably Pat had something to do with the devising of the master plan to evict Harry. After school one lovely spring day in March 1970, mum practically leapt on me as I walked in after school.

'Terry, Terry!' she said. 'I would have asked Jack but he's not here. I need your help. Terry... bloody Jack's doing something at school just when I need him, but you'll do...' (Jack was taking four CSE's and mum did not even know what he was doing.)

'I need your help,' she said again. 'Look, if you get your dad's signature on this bit of paper, the house will be mine! We'll be shot of the bugger! Terry, you've got to do this for me.'

'What?' I said, confused. 'What are you going on about? He'll never sign that.'

'Look,' she said. 'This is a Transfer of Tenancy form. If he signs this, here, then the house will be mine.'

'But he'll never sign it,' I repeated, reluctantly taking the document from her.

'No,' she said, her eyes gleaming with excitement. 'But he'll sign THIS!' She was holding a letter one of us had brought home from school about a trip to Brighton. She had rescued it from the bin. She continued, gabbling on about how she was going to stick the two forms together - the trip paper would be on top of the Tenancy Transfer form. She would cut a hole in the top form and when he signed it he would really be signing the tenancy form! Simple!

I looked at her. 'Well good luck,' I said, handing her back the form. 'I hope for your sake it works.'

'No, no, no, Terry,' she said. 'I'm not giving it to him, you are!'

The Master Plan had to work. I had been nagged and bullied into presenting the form(s) to him. I did not want to do it, for dad could in theory still give me a beating, but then I remembered the day of the challenge and how he had meekly sat down again, and anyway, perhaps this was worth a go, to get rid of the old man would certainly be good - one less alcoholic to put up with and peace from mum if nothing else.

The chosen night came, and he was thankfully, very drunk. She had seen him driving up the road half on the pavement so she knew the time was right. She had cooked him a dinner and he had just finished and was sitting watching television with a bottle of whisky. The time was now! Mum thrust the form into my hand along with a pen and practically pushed me from the kitchen into the living room.

I approached him. 'Can you sign this? It's a school trip.'

'What's that, son?' he looked up at me, very drunk, unfocused eyes.

I handed him the paper. It was so obvious - the cut out slit was jumping out of the paper obscenely at me; surely he too would spot it. He must see it! How could he not see it? He was staring at the form, he looked as if he was studying it intently. Then he took the pen from me and slowly, deliberately, he began to sign his name where I was pointing.

'No - a bit lower,' I said. I was really chancing my luck here! He slowly signed it, then slumped back in the chair. I grabbed the paper and went through to the kitchen. Mum was there, so excited she could hardly contain herself. I gave her the form, she glanced at it, grinned broadly and then ripped the top copy off. There, in all its glory, was the Transfer of Tenancy form, duly signed by Harry. He had signed away the tenancy to mum.

'It's mine!' she yelled, and tore into the living room. 'The house is mine, you bastard! You've got to get out now. This is My House!' She danced around the room triumphantly, waving her form, the happiest day of her life. She leant over so that her face was inches away from his. 'This is my house now,' she said poking him with every word. 'Look - you've signed it all over to me, and I want you out! Pack your fucking bags and go!'

And so it was that Harry packed his bags a few days later and left in his car. He did not appear to make any fuss or try and fight the trickery that had resulted in him losing his home. He just accepted it benignly, almost as if it was an excuse to go - to find some peace and happiness in his remaining years. We did not actually see him leave and he left no goodbyes for the boys whom he had brought up practically as if they were his own sons, but absolutely everything of his had gone. It was as if he finally gave in, threw in the towel, admitted defeat in this loveless life he had lived. It was really for good this time.

Mum thought life was going to be great now. She was free. But in practise, she had lost her drinking partner and although she religiously made trips up to the pub and met up with Pat a lot of the time, she was for most of the time, bored and lonely and after a few months she became more and more depressed. We were her victims now and she argued with us all the time. When we ignored her (which we did often) she tried more desperate measures and her own brand of suicide attempts restarted. She began her old tricks again, pretending to overdose and lying dramatically on her bed, shouting down to us that we would be sorry when she was gone! We were probably taking a gamble, but we were always pretty confident that she had not taken anything at all. If we went upstairs to investigate we would find the pill bottles empty on the bed beside her and carefully tucked under the pillow would be a mound of tablets. She would be lying out on her front, feigning unconsciousness.

'Have a nice sleep,' we would say as we went out, closing the door behind us.

'You bastards!' she would scream after us, suddenly very conscious, and something would be hurled at the door! We never took it seriously, somehow we just knew that she would never do it for real. She also insisted that she was terminally ill - she had cancer, only weeks to live! Again we had to ignore her - we could just see straight through her stories. But she was sick, we knew that and she just did not know how to get attention any other way.

Eventually Pat, Jack and I persuaded her to go to the hospital again to dry out. We had three silent weeks at home while she was away. Jack was sixteen now and had left school. He was working as an apprentice in a garage. I had to continue at school for another two terms and would be able to leave school after Easter 1971. I was one of the last year that were able to leave school at fifteen, without even entering the fifth form. But I would not be attending that much and it was unlikely the school would chase after me!

Angus was approaching the end of junior school and was starting the secondary school in September. I wondered if he would do better than Jack and me. It seemed very doubtful.

When mum returned she was wonderfully sober. She had lost her job but she quickly got another, cleaning in local offices and for a few months she was a real mum. She bought me a jumper - a new one, not from a jumble sale and she was kind and funny and made us laugh. She was such a different person when she was not drinking. It was nice to see the other side of her. She was also back in time to accompany me to court where the local magistrate eventually heard about the incident with the coal lorries - that old news that seemed to have happened a lifetime ago and had been delayed so often. He heard how the men had laid in wait for the little thugs who were damaging their property! Probation reports had been prepared but there was no mention of my home life, only poor progress at school, arrogance and aggression. I was conditionally discharged for one year and my driving licence, which I was still two years too young to have, was endorsed!

Mum stayed relatively sober for quite a few weeks but we knew underneath it all we were only on borrowed time. One day, we knew for certain, we would return to a dark, cold house and the familiar routine would start all over again. As young teenagers we were now acutely aware that there was no cure for alcoholics, only total abstinence and no matter what we said or did, no matter how much we tried to persuade our mum, she would not even admit there was a problem to be addressed.

****

Easter 1971 was a long time coming but when it did I left school, said farewell to the bicycle sheds where I had spent so much time and started a job. I was to follow Jack as an apprentice mechanic but after three weeks the garage allocated to me went into receivership and I was out of a job! Mum found out about a vacancy at a local printing firm. I went along for an informal interview and was offered work. I never knew why I was so terrible, why I could not concentrate for more than five minutes or so, but I must have been dreadful - the employee from hell. I stood at a bench with a long line of others, assembling tiny bits of typing components. I thought it was the most boring thing I had ever done. I had never been so fed up and uninspired in my life. It was only a matter of weeks before I was summoned to the boss's office.

I laughed cockily as I was led away and called out to the others that it was obviously promotion for me!

The Boss was not a happy man. Since I had started on the Bench the spot checks had been appalling and faults were found in almost every piece that had filtered through my hands. Was I thick? Was I stupid? No answer. He changed my job.

I was to transfer to the Paint Shop.

I boasted wildly to everyone that I had been removed from the Bench and was now in the Paint Shop. It was very slightly alarming that most of the employees were either people with learning difficulties or foreigners who did not speak English. All I had to do now was dip things into large vats of paint and hang them up to dry. But I could not even do that sensibly and before long I was throwing paint at fellow workers, whizzing paint pots around and I even painted one of the walls a nice bright yellow. A few days later I was summoned again. Now I was sacked!

Mum was as near to worried about me as she could be. Jack had held down his job for over a year and was working well, learning and on the road to qualification, but I was turning into a nightmare. When I was sixteen I bought myself a little moped, mainly so that I could travel the couple of miles to my new job. Now I was a labourer at a sheet metal firm where we made aluminium bus shelters. It was not a well paid job but the firm was a small family affair and the owners were very kind to me. They sympathised with me in some strange way and continually forgave me for being late and abusing their kindness. Gradually I began to respect them in my own odd way and they in turn gradually put up my pay. It was not challenging work at all but it was relaxed, I was working with a friend from school and the Taylors were good employers. They also had a son who often helped out in the sheds. When he was imprisoned for armed robbery I began to understand their compassion and understanding for me. But there really was no excuse for their son. He had been brought up well in the arms of a caring family and he really had let them down.

Mum was still plodding along in her usual state - sometimes not at home because she was out with Pat, drinking; sometimes she was at home with a variety of friends sprawled over the chairs, in various forms of intoxication. Sometimes she was absolutely fine, cooking a meal in the kitchen as I arrived home from work. It was always a good sign if the windows were heavy with condensation - that meant she was at home, cooking our tea and she was pretty sober. Once I arrived back to find her entertaining two Mormons. They had erected a huge screen in the living room and were showing her a cine-film on their way of life. In the kitchen they had demonstrated how to make popcorn and when I came in we all sat down and ate it. Why on earth she had invited them in I could not understand but she must have been lonely and simply enjoyed the company.

Then she acquired herself a boyfriend, a little Irish chap called Denny. He suffered a great deal under the wrath of our mum but he took it all as part of his lot and was blindingly loyal to her. Jack, Angus and I resented him very much. Mum divorced Harry in early 1972 and Denny supported her throughout it all, but the last thing we wanted was another heavy drinker around again.

I wonder if mum was ever really happy throughout her life. She seemed to struggle on from one disaster to another. She took huge quantities of tablets - pills to make her sleep, pills to wake her up, pills to cheer her up, pills to calm her down....she was a walking, rattling mix of chemicals, soaking it all up with bottles of drink. It was as if the doctor just prescribed what took his fancy: Take three a day until you're in orbit! Mum often was.

So we began living through a period of relative stability, but it was only because both Jack and I were earning money and financially supporting mum. She relied on us heavily. When sober she had a heart of gold and was swindled easily whenever she heard a sob story. Pat was an alcoholic waster who continuously fed mum stories of how she was about to be evicted because she could not pay her rent, she had to sell her television, the bailiffs were on their way... and mum provided her with money and even gave her the moped I had given her as a present when I bought a proper motorbike! I was livid, but mum insisted it was only for a couple of weeks - so that Pat's son could get to work, for his car had broken down. We never saw the moped again. It was even more galling to know that Jack and I were providing the cash to feed her generosity. But there was absolutely nothing we could do about it. We were just bystanders.

Mum was an impulsive woman at the best of times. Working in the sheds one summer's day, I was really surprised to hear her voice outside, chatting to Mrs Taylor, the proprietor. I stepped outside curiously and stood there watching them talking. They beckoned me over. Mum said, as if it were a totally normal occurrence, that we were off on holiday to Jersey! We had never had a holiday in our lives. I was full of questions and wanted answers but she just bundled me into a waiting taxi, where Angus was sitting with a huge bag on his knees.

'I'll tell you everything later,' was all she would say. 'Come on or we'll miss the flight.'

The flight?!! What was going on? Before I could draw breath we were at Gatwick Airport and we flew out to Jersey within two hours. Mum explained that she had put a bet on the National and had won enough for a holiday. She had tried to persuade Jack to come too but he had not wanted to know. It was all arranged, she said, just for the three of us. We were to stay in a lovely hotel and have a week away from it all. Well, thank you Red Rum, I thought as I looked out of the window, watching the little island of Jersey getting bigger.

When we arrived reality hit us. There was no hotel arranged, we jumped into a passing taxi and started hotel hunting. Luckily there were vacancies and we did actually spend quite a pleasant week, strolling along the beaches, walking round the town, eating tasty meals and I became infatuated with a young waitress who must have been about nineteen. Mum disappeared off and had her hair done and Angus and I enjoyed it all immensely. I was ready to get home after the week but it had been the experience of a lifetime.

If mum was disappointed that Jack had not wanted to join us she never let it show. She felt she had given us a wonderful treat and she revelled in the glory of that week in Jersey for ages. I suppose it might have been her way of showing how much she really thought of her boys.

She never wanted us to leave her, despite her boyfriend, and we never let her know that we had new interests in our lives - girls!

Chapter 10

Jack met his girlfriend, Janet, at a local pub but she had also attended the same secondary school as us, a year younger than me. He told her little about conditions at our home and he tried his very best for her - he only ever wanted to be normal. After passing his driving test, he bought himself a car. It all helped to impress Janet and her parents. I knew Janet from school and just could not see what Jack saw in her. She was a good time girl who wanted glamour, clothes, fun and a wealthy man to spend all his money on her. But Jack was smitten and there was no one else for him for years. Janet even made a play for me once. You really could not trust the girl and there were many occasions when she flirted outrageously with other men, but Jack would have been furious with me if I had said anything, so I just watched him from afar as he continued to see Janet. Perhaps it was as close to love as Jack had ever been but in reality she was the worst type of person to try and take on someone like Jack and all the emotional hang ups and baggage that came with him.

In April 1973 Trevor appeared at our door one afternoon. He broke up any semblance of peace and normality that there was. He had been released from prison a few months before after serving three years for robbery. I do not know why the sentence was so light. If I had been the judge I would have locked him up and thrown away the key. He was a complete and utter thug, from the dredges of Scottish society and we just wished he would forget about us and leave us alone. He was even more pugnacious now than he had been in 1969 when we had last had the pleasure of his company. His head was shaven and his arms were covered in tattoos and scars. Even mum did not seem as keen on him as before but he was family, and in he came.

Trevor boasted about his crime - how he had held a publican by his collar with a knife pressed against his throat in Glasgow and as he had pushed, ever so gently, the skin had split and blood had trickled out. The best bit was when he produced his gun - the old boy had handed over everything then! It had been brilliant. Prison had been a great place - he had picked up tips for new crimes and it was awash with drugs there. For free board and lodging you could not beat it. He showed us the tracks on his arms where heroin had flowed freely and offered some to us. But he was not addicted, he said, he could beat any drug anytime. Jack and I listened but we could not be impressed. His words depressed us. The life we had definitely seemed preferable to all that. But we smiled and joined in, kept Trevor happy.

Trevor moved into dad's old room and made himself at home. Before long mum started arguing with him. It did not occur to her that he was twice her size, a violent antagonistic miscreant who thought nothing of stabbing and killing. When she had had a few drinks Trevor, her nephew, son of her favourite sister, became the person she needed to abuse and fight with. Trevor, a hard drinker too, did not need much encouragement for a fight and he lashed back at her. They shouted at each other continually.

Glynis made an appearance a few weeks later, five months pregnant and still trying to make a go of their marriage. Why the poor girl bothered we just could not understand. I felt really sorry for her - to think she was having Trevor's baby! How could he ever be a decent father? But then who was I to judge who was a satisfactory father or not?

One evening Trevor and Glynis had the most violent argument in the living room. Mum could not resist interfering and she blindly took Glynis's side. Trevor struck both of them hard round their faces and pushed his wife around a bit. Angus disappeared immediately, along with Blackie who was barking wildly. Trevor stormed out and went up the pub.

I was seventeen and a half now and I spent most of my evenings with two mates a few miles away, lads who I had gone to school with and now worked with at the Taylors'. We all owned motor bikes and thinking back on it we must have appeared quite menacing, with our long unkempt hair, torn jeans and leather jackets and I was the scruffiest of the lot! I sat astride a large Triumph motor bike - the best in the world - but I was only ever a lamb in lion's clothing and would never have hurt anyone.

Sometimes we joined the regular bikers for day trips to Devil's Dyke, near Brighton, we frequented all the local pubs that would have us and we poured scorn on those of the oppostite faction - the skinheads, fashionably dressed in their huge collared flamboyant shirts and heavy overcoats. The air was heavy with discos and the sound of Alice Cooper, Cockney Rebel and Derek and the Dominos. They were memorable days, the early seventies - the beginning of the best years of my life, though I did not know it then. I was able to accept the poor life at home now for I could escape from it whenever I wanted.

I arrived home that evening about quarter to twelve to find mum and Glynis in the living room discussing Trevor. Immediately they recounted what had happened earlier in the evening. Glynis was distraught and kept crying. Mum, very drunk, was livid. Trevor was a bastard. Look what he had done to their faces and poor Glynis pregnant too, she could have lost the baby! SHE would not stand for that, Glynis should leave him now. (Yes, I thought, just like you did all those years ago!)

A knock on the back door. I got up and went over to open it. 'I want to speak to my wife,' said Trevor.

'Just go away,' I said. 'I think you've done enough damage tonight.'

Trevor was high on drink and drugs. He lunged forward to

grab me and I pushed him away. Before I knew it we were punching hell out of each other in the back garden. He was so strong, he had my throat and was twisting as hard as he could. He yelled and spat into my face: lights went on next door. At one point he lost his balance and we both fell heavily to the ground. I managed to swing myself over and sat on top of him, punching his face as hard as I could, beating his head on the ground. But Trevor struggled up, pushed me aside and tossed me on to the grass like a rag doll. His finger nail had split the skin under my nose and I was bleeding. Distracted by the dripping blood and trying to locate the source of my bleeding, Trevor barged past me and ran into the kitchen. He was going to see Glynis no matter what.

Mum was standing in front of the girl, all five foot nothing of her, trying to protect Glynis from a madman. From nowhere Trevor produced a glistening knife and as I reached the living room he plunged it right into mum's chest. In what seemed like slow motion, she clutched herself, blindly staggered forwards, then collapsed. Glynis screamed, breaking the terror of the situation and I grabbed Trevor from behind. I found the strength to hold him for just a few seconds, then I felt assistance from beside me and turned to see Jack. Jack had appeared from nowhere and he was the most welcome sight. Relief flooded through me, for together we found the strength to control Trevor. We managed to get him down on the floor and Jack yelled at Angus to go next door and call for an ambulance. Glynis was crying over her protector's body now. Mum was crumpled in a little heap, twitching, blood seeping from her wound, red on the carpet. Jack and I took it in turns to punch Trevor as hard as we could. All the pent up frustration of so many years went into the beating Trevor received that night. We could have killed him had we not been interrupted.

The police arrived first - they roughly released Trevor from us, and he now shouted and kicked out at everyone. Ambulance men appeared and swiftly attended to mum. As the police dragged Trevor, still struggling wildly, up the back garden path our eyes met. 'I'll be back for you, Terry! Never forget this - I'll be back to get you!' They were the last words I ever heard him say and they were to haunt me for the rest of my life.

Mum was carried away on a stretcher. No one went with her. Glynis must have shed pints of tears that night and Jack and I consoled her as best we could. Jack rang the hospital at three in the morning and they said mum was comfortable, despite bruising and a punctured collapsed lung. She was a very lucky lady and she would live. We would visit in the morning.

****

By the end of the year I too had a girlfriend. I never knew why she bothered with me but for some reason she pursued me from our second meeting. Like Janet, Jack's girlfriend, Sophie came from a nice respectable family, and like Jack, I made absolutely sure that she never visited my house, even though she only lived a few hundred yards away. I never really put myself out for Sophie and often did not keep to planned arrangements but she was always there. We became a couple and she was happy to go everywhere on the back of my motor bike!

At some point around this time, mum was charged with theft. It appeared that she had been partying for days in Pat's house - when she finally sobered up enough to leave, Pat found her diamond rings had vanished. Pat and her husband searched high and low for the valuable rings, they had a witness who said she had actually seen mum removing the rings from the woman's finger, but they could not find them. Mum was accused of stealing them. The police turned up, charged and arrested her. It was a dreadfully embarrassing time when mum went to court - it was front page news in the local papers, there in black and white for everyone to see - Sophie and her family saw it, just about the whole world saw it! Mum was guilty - I knew she was, although she strongly denied it. Those rings could have been pawned or sold and traded for alcohol. Pat was now mum's enemy from hell - we had abusive phone calls at night (the phone: our new acquisition, but only until the bill arrived and we were disconnected!) and she screamed and cursed mum if she saw her at the shops. But the rings were never found and lack of evidence meant mum was acquitted. Two sparkling diamond rings had probably been thrown down a drain and to this day remain unfound in the filth of the sewers! It was mum's last big incident, for she remained almost blissfully unaware of her own fast approaching nemesis.

In the hedonistic summer of 1974, when Gary Glitter was at his height and teenagers were all bopping to T Rex at discos and church youth clubs, Sophie and I went to the cinema one Sunday evening. It was a hot balmy night in July and she was happy because her exams at school had all finished and she was on an extended holiday until she started the sixth form. (How could anyone wish to stay on at school a moment longer than absolutely necessary?)

For some strange reason I was restless that evening and sensed something was amiss. I could not explain what it was but I could not concentrate on the film at all and felt I was watching the screen through a film of mist. I had left mum at home that afternoon in a strange melancholy mood. She had been murmuring that she wished she had a daughter and she missed Glynis. Glynis was a mum herself now, she had a baby daughter and mum kept repeating over and over that she had thrown away her only chance of having a daughter. I said to her that it was not her fault our real dad had died but she looked at me with sad watery eyes and said I just did not understand. She asked me where I was going as I pulled my jacket on and I just said: 'Out', as is customary among teenagers starting to grab at independence. She nodded slowly. She knew I was going out with Sophie. Benignly she had had to accept the existence of our girlfriends though she never mentioned them or asked to meet them.

Before the film finished I turned to Sophie and whispered that we had to leave. She was reluctant and angry but she followed me out and I took her home. I drove back to my house and locked my bike in the garage. Clutching my helmet I went inside. All was dark and calm, mum and Angus were both in bed. So everything was all right. I had thought for a moment that I had had a premonition of impending doom. But no, all was peaceful after all.

Monday morning came. Jack and I were not good at getting up and mum always had a fight on her hands to get us up and off to work. This morning she was unusually agitated and Jack could sense trouble. So he was up and away with minimal fuss. Eventually I struggled downstairs to get ready for work. Mum was coming up the stairs. 'Terry, I've got a dreadful headache,' she said, clutching the side of her head. 'I'm going back to bed for a bit.'

I signalled to Angus to get up and away, for he still shared a bedroom with her - to leave her in peace. We sat together downstairs with a cup of tea and I said I would just check on mum before I left for work. Angus was nearly fifteen, a regular truant from school and he fitted in with us better now than ever before, although he never lost his plumpness. Mum was asleep, sound asleep. I tried to rouse her, but she made no response at all. Angus came up and we both stood looking down at her. What could be wrong? We both tried to wake her but her breathing was strange now, a noisy raspy breathing. We were both getting a little alarmed. I went next door and rang the doctor.

The doctor's receptionist was cool and calm. She suggested mum had a virus that was going around. 'When she wakes, make sure she has lots to drink and an aspirin,' she suggested.

But an hour later we still could not rouse mum at all. She was in a really deep sleep, still making the strange noises, and now she had lost all control of her bodily functions. There was an awful odour in the room. This seemed to be more than a viral infection. I rang the doctor's again. The same receptionist now suggested that mum had gastro-enteritis, apparently that was going around too. Again, give her lots to drink when she awakens. 'But she won't wake up - it's as if she's unconscious,' I said. Very reluctantly, with an exasperated sigh, the receptionist agreed to send the doctor out after morning surgery.

I removed the hard lump from under mum's bedcovers and placed the half bottle of gin carefully in the wardrobe.

The doctor, the very same one who had treated my impetigo sores, turned up at eleven thirty. He was elderly and bored. He seemed irritated that we had called him out. I led him upstairs and left him in the bedroom with mum. He reappeared a minute later, and trotted down the stairs with an urgency he had not had before. 'I think I'll call an ambulance and get your mum into hospital,' he said. 'May I use the phone?'

'Next door,' I said and Angus led him round to the very patient and long-suffering neighbour who must have endured so much over the years living next to us!

The ambulance came swiftly and took mum away, still deeply unconscious. I immediately drove up to Jack's work and he left to join in the confusion at home. The three of us went up to the hospital in the afternoon and were shocked by what we saw: Mum was all wired up to various pieces of equipment. She had tubes here, there and everywhere and the doctor explained they were draining fluid from her spine as we spoke. I asked tentatively what was wrong with her and they matter of factly said that they believed she had a cerebral haemorrhage. In my youthful ignorance, it meant very little to me then. I remember Jack saying: 'But she will get better, won't she?' and the doctor carefully replied that they were very concerned about her, but her heart was strong and the next few days would tell.

The child within me just wanted her to get up and be fine, but the growing man inside began to acknowledge the realisation that this probably would not happen. But we never discussed it - Jack, Angus and me - we stood there looking down at our mum, face pale, slightly lined now round the mouth and eyes. She was so thin, the fragility of her skeletal form noticed more than ever. Occasionally her mouth twitched, almost as if she were smoking a cigarette in her dreams. Should not smoke so much, I thought - should not drink so much either......

We had to inform the relatives in Scotland for as the next day passed it became clear that the doctors were extremely concerned. Mum still had not regained consciousness and they now felt there was little they could do except wait. But we understood the gravity in their tone, we knew it was serious. Within two days mum's relations swept in and took control. Two of her brothers (not Don) and four sisters (one of whom was Trevor's mother) had come to do their duty. Two of them were alcoholics and the house turned into one big drinking place. On the fourth day of mum's hospitalisation a cousin arrived to join her dad - Pauline, an attractive young girl, but she did not really know our mum and had no idea of what she was really like.

Mum died exactly a week later; three of her sisters had been dutifully sitting with her when she died and they came back and told us what had happened. She had just slipped peacefully away. She had never regained consciousness. Jack, Angus and I just stood there in the kitchen, listening. In basic terms, mum had had a stroke, probably brought on by years of heavy drinking. She was only forty eight. It seemed such a waste. She would never see us all as men, she would never be a grandmother. So this was definitely, finally, without any doubt whatsoever, the end. It really was all over now.

What can you say when your mum dies? That you are sad, sorry, regretful, guilty? I do not know what Jack and Angus thought, for we never discussed it. I think we were bereft of any deep meaningful feelings, struck emotionless from years of heavy endurance. I think we still are. But I lay in bed at night and tried to work out my thoughts and feelings, the many images of transition that haunt all my memories of her.

Sad: Yes, I was sad, for she was our mum and underneath all her problems I must have loved her. When sober she was funny and happy and she cared deeply for us. She would never have carried on in those early days especially, if it had not been for us. We had had good times, we had had times of togetherness.

Sorry: Was I sorry she was gone? I could not say, for it seemed in a way as if a curtain had been lifted up from our family and we were set free. I could not say if I was sorry. But I was sorry for her - such an addictive person: addicted to drink, probably addicted to so many of those pills that she duped the doctors into prescribing for her - perhaps I was sorry.

Regretful: Yes, I was certainly regretful. What a childhood she had put us through. Her and Harry - together we had lived in impecunity in a hell on earth. Yes, I was regretful of the aggression, of the neglect, the poverty, the alcoholism. So many times I had just wanted to be like all those other children, going home to nice warm homes with normal parents. There had been so many nights when I had cried myself to sleep in the dark. I had endured such beatings that I thought I would die. I had often been so hungry and cold. I had hated being a child. Once I had read something in a magazine about a girl whose mother had been an alcoholic and she and her father had battled to keep the family together - but that was just one sick parent, at least she had had her father there for her. We had had no one.

Guilty: Perhaps, just a little. Maybe we could have cared a little more once we were grown up. Maybe we could have got more help for her....but then she was probably past help. Would she have co-operated? It seemed extremely unlikely. Even up to the last she was not remorseful. She had insisted she was not an alcoholic, that she controlled her drinking, and like the pills, a little drink was 'for her nerves.' She never acknowledged the dreadful results of prolonged inebriation. I could sympathise with Harry now - our mother was an almost impossible woman to live with. She made his life a total misery too. How might he have been if he had not managed to tie himself up with her? But still I can not hate her - all she did to us, or allowed to happen to us - even now I can not find hate in my heart. My memories now are a mixture of regret and compassion but she was, and always will be, our mum.

At the time I was never really angry - never experienced that bitter anger that I could have had. It just never came. Right to the end I still felt our mother was a victim of circumstances - that in a different time things could have been so different. She betrayed us so many times, let us down, lied and was happy for us to take the blame for her actions, but I do not think she ever intended us to suffer the way we did - she simply did not notice.

We received a telegram from Harry: 'Sorry to hear of your mother's death. Will be in touch; See you soon'. He had heard from a neighbour who worked near to him in London. We did not see him soon - it was another four years before he made contact with us again ('Totally, sober now, Terry son, I never touch spirits now!' No, but he still enjoyed a drink. There was to be no real 'cure' for Harry, although remarkably, he lived to be quite an old man. I phoned him recently, not long before he died - he lived with his fourth wife in retirement. He must have been almost eighty and he was too drunk to even get to the phone!)

The funeral had to be arranged and we went through it all like actors in a macabre play. Sadly, mum was buried the day after Angus's fifteenth birthday. She had a good Catholic service and abstract words were said about her by a priest. I looked around all the faces as we stood at the graveside. Denny was not there. He had completely disappeared. From the day mum had been admitted to hospital he had just vanished from our lives. That was sad, for he had played a major part in mum's last year or so and he should have been there but we had never made it easy for him to share our family life. We had never welcomed him or said many kind words to him. He probably thought he would be shunned so he stayed away. I knew he was aware of her death for Angus had bumped into him in the town and Denny had asked how we all were. He already knew she had died. Pat did not turn up either, but there was a small wreath 'from all your friends in The Crown.'

Not that long after mum's death Sophie and I spotted Denny sitting in a bus shelter, sad and alone, clutching a bag of chips. I still had this hang up about him, as if he were an intruder and an outsider but something deep inside me insisted that the ethical thing to do was to approach him. I asked him how he was. To my complete surprise Denny could hardly look up at me and then suddenly he started crying. He could not find many words to say but I knew for sure that he must have really thought a lot of mum and I admired him so much more then. He was the one and only person who shed a tear for my mother. It was even more touching when, just before he went back to Ireland, I visited mum's grave and saw one plastic red rose carefully placed there. I knew it was from Denny and it was a touching gesture of goodbye from her final companion.

The relatives made plans to leave and they literally stripped our house of ornaments and jewellery, all taken 'as a keepsake, in remembrance of our dear Alice'; mum's watch, rings, necklace, any decent clothes. They were all packed into two vast suitcases. Pauline was insensitive enough to walk around in mum's slippers and dressing gown, remarking on what a coincidence it was that they were both the same size, and she needed a new dressing gown. They went into the suitcases too.

We had not owned much as it was but as our relatives walked up the road, laden down with their heavy bags, dragging two suitcases on wheels, we walked around our now very bare house. My bedroom curtains had gone. They had hung up some old brown material instead! Thinking back on it, it seems unbelievable but at the time the three of us accepted it all without question. After all, we would have no use for all mum's things - they could take what they wanted. Only one aunt, the fiercely anti-alcohol Madge, remained above it all.

She was our sole comforter and the only relation whose love and friendship I continue to value to this day. At the time we just had to carry on with our lives and the emptiness and loneliness really hit me for the first time. What would become of us now? Where did we go from here? It did not take long for the wheels of destiny to be set in motion though and Jack arranged for the tenancy of the house to be transferred into his name. Within a few days of mum's funeral Janet abandoned all her plans of college and moved in.

Janet was a bitch, as insensitive as some of our relatives who had swept in like jackdaws. She must have been very satisfied that Jack's mother had died for the path was now clear for them to marry. To cap it all Jack was now a tenant with a four bedroom house and she wanted it for them. She carefully began weaving her plans, they started arranging their wedding for a couple of months time and then, once safely married, she started her campaign of getting Angus and me out and unfortunately there was nothing anyone could do about it. I had never known such a nasty, vindictive person as Janet. Her worst fear was that I may try and move Sophie in and she certainly was not standing for that: she was the wife of the tenant now and she had far more rights to be there than Angus or me! She threatened us with solicitor's letters and injunctions, she phoned Sophie accusingly, to state her case and make quite sure it was absolutely clear whose house it was now! Legally she was right but morally it seemed deeply repugnant.

Jack was weak and hopelessly in love for the first time. He wanted to stand by me but he had to stand by Janet. He sat silently as rows raged above his head between Janet, Sophie and me. He was totally torn between loyalty towards his brother and love for Janet. It was becoming impossible for me to be there, impossible for Angus to be there and gradually over a few short weeks our tight relationship broke down - eroded to dust as if it had never been. It was Jack and Janet's house now. If I ate anything she wanted to know where I had got it from - was I touching the food she had bought, which was just for her and Jack? Although I paid them a little money for my keep, they always waited until I had gone out for the evening before cooking their meal, so now, unless I made it myself, I never ate a hot dinner. Effectively they managed to evict me.

Jack had made his choice: It had a profound effect on me, and Sophie, whom I now turned to. After all Jack and I had been through together, all that we had endured, to think he could have chosen her instead of me, that he did not once stand up for me. When with Janet he was on her side: yes it was their house, he would agree and they bought things and rearranged furniture, redecorated and smooched around like young lovers do. When with me he was on my side: no, he did not want to throw me out, yes he wanted me to stay, he would talk to Janet and perhaps I could remain (in my home) until I found somewhere for myself, no he was not forcing me out. But Jack betrayed me, and he betrayed Angus to a certain extent. Love won at the end of the day and it took a long, long time for me to forgive him for it. I always thought Jack and I were bonded through our endurance and our unspoken secrets, but evidently he now thought quite differently. Jack just pulled a blind down on his past and started anew. It was the biggest single shock of my life, that Jack had turned against me. I knew from that moment that we would not be growing old together. But in a way it forced me to grow up too, the whole sorry episode put a final seal on my childhood and I was standing on my own two feet, as an independent adult, for the first time.

And so it was that Jack and Janet started their married life in our family home. Blackie, quite an old smelly dog now, was put to sleep (I swear Janet could not bare him being in her house!) and Angus was also forced out by them a few weeks later. Janet and Jack found Angus very difficult, dishonest and deceitful. They wanted to use him as their messenger boy, for he was unemployed and lethargic throughout his long lonely days. But Angus merely found other uses for the rent money Janet had put by so carefully. He always swore blind that he had not touched a penny, but they knew.... Angus was a victim of circumstances, bitter and resentful and Jack, always fired along by Janet, told Angus he had to go. Angus caught the coach to Scotland, to stay with Auntie Madge, the aunt who had provided much love and stability for him throughout his formative years. He hoped to make a new life for himself, get a job - perhaps even work in the mines.

So I was left alone - well not entirely alone, for Sophie, as always, was there and the local council, unusually, took pity on us and offered us a tiny railway cottage in Redhill, not very far from St Anne's (which was demolished soon after and became a huge sprawl of modern urban housing). Within months we, too, had married. We had practically nothing to do with Jack and Janet for seven years and their young daughters were sadly strangers to us. When Angus returned after a few months (initially for a short while - there was no work in Scotland) he moved in with Sophie and me and there he stayed for the next few years. Gradually Angus began to find his feet - maybe we gave him the security he craved just in time, and, despite a few minor brushes with the law, he was able to secure employment and started dating the odd girl. Eventually he was financially able to buy his own flat and moved in with a new wife in 1984. Now he raises two children of his own. Sophie and I considered it quite an achievement, for we were only young ourselves when we took him in, but Angus has emerged from everything like the phoenix from the ashes - and now he is an ordinary family man. What would have happened to Angus otherwise?

****

All stories must have the essence of a happy ending - especially a childhood as teeming as ours was with appalling social depravity and endless misery. Sadly, it did all end in tears for Jack and Janet. They divorced after seven or eight years of marriage and Jack effectively lost much contact with his two girls, who started a new life with Janet's parents at the age of six and four. Neither Jack nor Janet fought for their children who almost seemed discarded, and I often wondered if Jack saw any parallels with his own childhood. Janet went on to marry twice more and started another family with her third husband. Jack had held a torch for her for so many years - she must have broken his heart.

I swear he does not know where he went wrong with Janet - but perhaps she merely fell out of love with him. I do not know if Jack will ever fully come to terms with all that has happened to him throughout his troubled life. How did all the childhood responsibility affect him? He is introverted and despondent much of the time, teeming with unspoken remarks that seem to cry out from behind his steely blue eyes. Jack is a depressed observer of life rather than a participant. He struggles to maintain a relationship with his two daughters, now grown up and disinterested to a certain extent in their absent father, and he tries hard to live happily with girlfriends who know so little of his past and all that we endured. He drinks too much and he knows it. Why is it that children of alcoholics so often turn to drink themselves in times of stress and depression? Is it conditioned upbringing or is it in the genes? Maybe it is a mixture of both. Perhaps real help and effective support will never be there for Jack, despite counselling, but he will always be my brother, no one can take away what we once shared, (although to this day we never discuss our childhood) and I shall always care for him.

Sophie and I went on to have five children over eighteen years; two boys and three girls - all of whom are growing up healthy and happy. We have seen the back of the notoriously troubled teenage years for the eldest and we all seem to have come through relatively unscarred. But then Sophie says that I too am a victim of my past, and there is probably enough locked inside of me to keep a psychologist in business for a year! We have had troubled times, seriously difficult times when we are totally unable to meet in the middle. There have been occasions when our marriage has practically been over, but that final thread just will not break. I have no real parental mould in which to lay the foundations for the upbringing of my own children and I have to believe that the way Sophie wants it done is the 'normal' way. And it is not trendy now to have 'normal' and 'abnormal' - those so called experts say we have to decide what is right for ourselves these days, but I really need someone to tell me: 'This is normal; this is right.' How can I know that what I want is wrong or peculiar? I have a problem with occasions such as birthdays and Christmas, yet I do not know why - it is just so difficult to partake. There have been really heavy issues for me to come to terms with. Maybe just by sharing it all with Sophie I have had some therapy. I have found myself at times almost laughing at incidents which upset me so much as a child.

But somehow along the way I lost my religion and the faith that my dad had long ago tried to install into his young boys. There was no spiritual protector for us and never an answer to my prayers, whispered in bed while tears rolled down my cheeks. I would smear them away angrily with the back of my hand, irritated that I could not stop my stupid crying. They were always tears in the dark, for I never wanted anyone to see a weakness in my armour.

It is almost beyond my comprehension to fully appreciate the fact that my eldest son has been bright enough, and wanted to go to university - so much fulfilment and security, so much life to live. He has a brilliant high flying career ahead of him in which he revels. My eldest daughter runs her own business which is going from strength to strength. In so many ways I re-lived my childhood through my own children's lives: I have played on the swings with them, kicked a ball about with them, read books with them, laughed and played with them in a way Harry and mum never did with us.

I always found it incredible that they could invite people home so casually. They know their home is always clean and tidy and their parents are friendly and respectable. Only once did two of my friends visit my childhood home and mum invited them in - almost sober, and she even made them something to eat while they waited for me to return from work. But then one of them cracked a joke. She thought they were laughing at her and she ended up throwing them out, shouting abuse after them as they ran - it was so embarrassing, for they thought she was mad!

Lack of education played a huge part in my life during the first ten years of my marriage and I became a man obsessed with getting to grips with English. I returned to evening classes for a year to catch up on so much that I had missed and ended up being able to pass the examinations to join the Ambulance Service. Why did I want to be an ambulanceman? So often the legacy left by alcoholic parents seems to result in their children becoming carers. Jack and I played our part in the caring and well-being of our mum and stepdad for so many years. It was almost programmed into us. It certainly helps me with my work now. I have an understanding of drinkers and their problems, the hopelessness and misery that goes with it, the depression and the suicide attempts, the lies and the secrets. I have to admit that I have little patience with any of them.

One of my proudest days was when I qualified as an ambulance paramedic - who would have believed it? Terry the school failure, now lifted out of poverty and into a prosperity no one would ever have thought possible.

Once, by bizarre chance, I took my old maths teacher in to hospital: 'I used to be in your class at school,' I said, as we drove along in the back of the ambulance; 'Did you?' he peered at me through his glasses but there was no spark of recognition. 'Well it certainly didn't do you any harm,' he said, smiling, satisfied, impressed that his pupil had done okay.

It would be an understatement to say that I was surprised and shocked when one day in 1985 we received a phone call from Scotland. It was a woman who said she was my half-sister! We spoke cautiously for some time and she visited soon after with all the documentation she needed to prove her story. She was the daughter of mum and the hotel manager from Largs - the man mum had often spoken of - the man who was going to abandon all for her, leave his wife and family and set her up in luxury. Jane had probably been conceived in a drunken haze and was born in 1949 in a convent. She had been adopted at six weeks old. She was the splitting image of our mother, she even talked like her! It was uncanny to say the least. But ironically, Jane had been the adopted daughter of publicans and she too was a heavy drinker with an aggression that we recognised all too well. It really must be something to do with the genes.

But what a secret! Mum kept it fervently until the day she died. She really must have thought her secret would die with her. It was even more remarkable knowing her as we did, for our mum could not keep a secret after a few drinks. But she kept this one, this one that mattered so much to her, this terrible scandal that had brought such shame on her. Auntie Madge confirmed the truth of it all. She had never mentioned it over the years but she had assumed we all knew about this half-sister. My thoughts went back to one of the last conversations I had with her before she died - was she thinking of Jane then?

Harry made me smile: oh yes, he said, he had always known there might be a daughter; Alice had mentioned it to him several times, but he had not really believed it - he thought it was the drink talking. I doubt it very much somehow that mum told Harry. I think her secret was etched on her very soul and telling him would have been like confiding in the devil's advocate.

****

Sitting in the garden with a glass of wine, looking up at the deep blue sky - the thin white trail of an aeroplane high above, curving round the arc of the world. Every now and then I smell the distinctive smell of freshly mown grass: yes, even now it takes me straight back to when I lived in the caravan at Newdigate, the old people playing bowls, dressed in their crisp clean whites and straw boaters. But I am reasonably content now. There is no more fear, no more real insecurity. Sophie and I have somehow endured well over twenty years of marriage and there is no greater joy than sitting back and reflecting on all that has gone and all that might come to be.

EPILOGUE

My crewmate and I are called to a house - there has been a fall. It is a grotty council house in a particularly seedy area. He bangs on the front door which is boarded up with hardboard. Old bed frames, a mattress and a broken, rusty washing machine litter the front garden. From somewhere deep inside a dog is barking.

'Ambulance!' I shout. 'Did someone call for an ambulance?'

Noises inside and the door is opened by a modern day Trevor. He is heavily tattooed, in a dirty white T shirt and jeans, unshaven, crew cut, earring, stinks of drink. He indicates to the bottom of the stairs and then disappears. We step into the most dreadful smell. A woman is lying over the bottom three stairs. She has fallen (or was she pushed?) and she is groaning slightly. She has a nasty cut on her head. She is drunk, she smells, in fact the whole place stinks. There is dog excrement smeared up the walls and newspapers and old clothes litter the floor.

We get her loaded up, then I return to tell her partner what is going on. I push open the living room door. Two small boys are huddled together in a cold cheerless room. They are grubby and neglected, their 'father' sits away from them, a can of lager in his hand, staring at the television. He looks up at me as I peep round the door. He grunts as I explain we are taking his wife into hospital. I look at the two little boys - two and three perhaps? They look up at me from their dirty chair, with big round soulful eyes and my heart goes out to them. It could have been us, Jack and me. We were those boys once, long ago. I have sat like that on a chair, watching my parents drink and fight. Does nothing change? Does it still go on, raw and dangerous, like it did for us? Be strong, boys, I think, you've just got to be strong and you'll make it... Children can survive adversity - I am living proof of that.

'Terry! What's keeping you? Come on!' I walk out to join my crew mate and sit pensively all the way to the hospital.

Then I do something that no one ever did for me when I was small. I make a telephone call.